MARKET LEADER

Practice File

D1373124

INTERMEDIATE
BUSINESS ENGLISH

David Cotton   David Falvey   Simon Kent

with *Talk business* pronunciation section
by John Rogers

Longman

FINANCIAL TIMES
World business newspaper.

Map of the Practice File

	Language work			Talk business	
	Vocabulary	**Language review**	**Writing**	**Sound work**	**Survival business English**
Unit 1 Globalisation page 2 / page 68	Words for talking about globalisation Phrasal verbs	Comparing	Replying to an order	**Individual sounds:** Pronunciation of comparative and superlative forms **Connected speech:** *as* Consonant–vowel links **Stress and intonation:** Stress in phrasal verbs	Telephoning Socialising 1
Unit 2 Brands page 6 / page 70	Words for talking about brands Words that go with *market*	Past simple and present perfect	Making recommendations	**Individual sounds:** Pronunciation of the *-ed* ending of regular verbs **Connected speech:** Consonant–vowel links **Stress and intonation:** Stress differences in related words /ə/ *schwa*	First-time meetings Informal conversation
Unit 3 Travel page 10 / page 72	Words for talking about travel	*Will*	Replying to letters of complaint	**Individual sounds:** *will* (contractions) (dark /l/) **Connected speech:** Disappearing sounds **Stress and intonation:** *Wh-* questions	Asking for agreement or confirmation Useful phrases
Unit 4 Advertising page 14 / page 74	Words for talking about advertising	Articles: *a, an, the*	Making complaints	**Individual sounds:** /eɪ/ vs /e/ **Connected speech:** How many words? **Stress and intonation:** Agreement and polite disagreement	Dealing with complaints Starting presentations
Unit 5 Employment page 18 / page 76	Words for talking about employment	Questions	Giving news to job applicants	**Individual sounds:** /ɒ/ vs /əʊ/ **Connected speech:** Sound changes **Stress and intonation:** Stress in three-syllable words	Managing meetings Asking for repetition
Unit 6 Trade page 22 / page 78	Words for talking about international trade	Conditions	Placing an order	**Individual sounds:** /ʊ/ vs /uː/ **Connected speech:** vowel–vowel link with /j/ **Stress and intonation:** Stress patterns Intonation in lists	Negotiating
Unit 7 Innovation page 26 / page 80	Words for talking about innovation	Passives	Replying to letters of enquiry	**Individual sounds:** /ɜː/ **Connected speech:** vowel–vowel link with /w/ **Stress and intonation:** Highlighting	Making presentations Insisting tactfully
Unit 8 Organisation page 30 / page 82	Words for talking about organisation	Noun combinations	Notices	**Individual sounds:** /ʌ/ **Connected speech:** Linking with /r/ **Stress and intonation:** Compound nouns	Conversation skills

The sounds of English: page 66   **Sounds and spelling**: page 66   **Shadowing**: page 67

	Language work			Talk business	
	Vocabulary	**Language review**	**Writing**	**Sound work**	**Survival business English**
Unit 9 Money page 34 / page 84	Words for talking about money and figures	Trends	Organising a report	**Individual sounds:** /aʊ/ vs /əʊ/ **Connected speech:** Weak forms: *was, were* **Stress and intonation:** 'Old' and 'new' information	Correcting information Describing trends
Unit 10 Ethics page 38 / page 86	Words for talking about business ethics	Narrating	Introducing a company's products or services	**Individual sounds:** /æ/ vs /ʌ/ **Connected speech:** Auxiliary verbs: strong and weak forms **Stress and intonation:** Stress patterns	Problem solving Tactful suggestions
Unit 11 Change page 42 / page 88	Words for talking about change	Reporting	Agendas and action minutes	**Individual sounds:** /v/ vs /w/ **Connected speech:** Contractions **Stress and intonation:** Sentence stress	Agreeing and disagreeing 1 Asking for clarification
Unit 12 Strategy page 46 / page 90	Words for talking about business strategies	Dependent prepositions	Reports	**Individual sounds:** /ɔː/ vs /əʊ/ **Connected speech:** Prepositions: weak forms **Stress and intonation:** Stress in word partnerships	Sounding decisive
Unit 13 Cultures page 50 / page 92	Socialising with business associates	Modal verbs	Invitations and thanking people for hospitality	**Individual sounds:** Spellings of the sound /iː/ **Connected speech:** Weak forms: modal verbs **Stress and intonation:** Expressing enthusiasm Expressing doubt or reservation	Socialising 2 Adding emphasis
Unit 14 Leadership page 54 / page 94	Words to describe character and skills	Relative clauses	Curricula vitae (resumes) and covering letters	**Individual sounds:** /θ/ vs /ð/ **Connected speech:** How many words? Making links **Stress and intonation:** Stress patterns in adjectives	Saying what you mean Giving explanations
Unit 15 Competition page 58 / page 96	Words for talking about competition	Talking about the future	Making bookings and confirming plans	**Individual sounds:** Odd-one-out (revision of a variety of vowel phonemes) Pronunciation of the letters *-ea-* **Connected speech:** Talking about the future **Stress and intonation:** Sentence stress	Making an appointment Agreeing and disagreeing 2
Unit 16 Quality page 62 / page 98	Words for talking about quality	Prepositions of time	Asking for payment	**Individual sounds:** Words ending in *-tion* or *-sion* **Connected speech:** Revision **Stress and intonation:** Intonation in complaints / replies to complaints	Polite requests in meetings Dealing with problems

Answer key: page 100 **Audio scripts:** page 116

Globalisation

Vocabulary

A Complete the passage about the US retailer *Wal-Mart* with appropriate words from the list.

acquisition	controlling interest	domestic	expansion
~~globalisation~~	joint ventures	overseas	targeted

Wal-Mart, the world's biggest retailer, increased its net earnings by almost 18% during its 4th quarter to 31 January. This was due to a large increase in its international profits. In early trading on the New York Stock Exchange, the shares rose by a dollar.

Wal-Mart is in the early stages of its *globalisation*[1] programme. In December, it entered Europe with the ....[2] of a German hypermarket chain, *Wertkauf*. ....[3] in other parts of the world has contributed to its profits. It has done well in Mexico, having bought a ....[4] in the *Cifra* chain last September. Wal-Mart has stores in Argentina, Brazil and Puerto Rico, and has ....[5] or franchises in China and Indonesia.

In its ....[6] market, the US, it has opened more superstores, which combine the out-of-town discount stores with a grocery department. These stores are ....[7] at customers wanting to shop at one time in one place.

Wal-Mart's international division is planning to add about 60 stores to the 603 it already has open. It will also continue to be on the lookout for suitable acquisitions in ....[8] markets. In the US, the company plans to add 26m sq. ft of retail floor space by opening new stores and superstores.

B The phrasal verbs below are used for telephoning. Match them with the correct meanings.

1	call back	a)	make contact
2	cut off	b)	find
3	get back to	c)	contact again later
4	get through	d)	wait
5	hang up	e)	talk louder
6	hold on	f)	telephone again
7	look up	g)	break contact
8	pick up	h)	answer
9	put through	i)	replace the receiver
10	speak up	j)	connect

C Put the phrasal verbs in exercise B in the correct order in a phone call.

Before call	Starting call	During call	Ending call	After call
				call back

D Complete these sentences with the phrasal verbs from exercise B. Make sure you use the correct tense.

1 If you don't know a number you can always ..*look*.......... it ..*up*.............. in the directory.
2 .... a minute, I'll see if she's free.
3 It took a long time but eventually I ....to him.
4 The switchboard .... me .... to the manager's office.
5 This is a terrible line. I can't hear you very well. You'll have to ....
6 I don't have the figures. I'll have to .... you tomorrow.
7 I can't talk now. I'll .... you .... later.
8 He's on his mobile and the signal is weak. That's why we keep getting ....
9 When you finish a call you ....
10 It's been ringing for ages. I wish she'd .... the phone.

Language review
Comparing

A Read the descriptions of two mobile phones. Write three sentences which explain the differences between the two phones.

For example: *The Cell XL1 is heavier than the Mobile XJ2.*

THE CELL XL1
Weight – 180 grams
Size – 7 cm by 14 cm by 3 cm
30 mins free calls every month
Calls billed by the second
2 year guarantee
PRICE £99

THE MOBILE XJ2
Weight – 100 grams
Size – 6 cm by 10 cm by 2 cm
30 mins free calls every month
Calls billed by the second
3 year guarantee
PRICE £150

B Write a short paragraph comparing one of your products (or services) or a product (or service) you know well with a product or service of a competitor.

Language work

C Read the following conversation between the Sales Manager and General Manager of a top soft drinks company. They are discussing where to take the top sales representatives for their sales incentive holiday, paid for by the company. There are five mistakes in the use of comparatives. Find them and correct them.

SUSAN:

I'm in favor of Tucson, Arizona. There's lots to do. It's an action-packed holiday. Horse-riding will appeal to the men and the women and the golf is great. Also, it'll be more cheap for the company.

KEVIN:

I hear what you're saying, Susan, but I think Mauritius is more better for a number of reasons. We're going in March. Mauritius will be hotter and dryer. It's more convenient. Although accommodation in Tucson is good, especially at the top-end of the market, quality accommodation in Mauritius is better. It's a different culture. The food is more varied. The place is just exoticer. Admittedly it will be more expensive, but the perceived value and incentive to the sales reps will be more great.

Writing
Replying to an order

Look at the Useful language in the box. Then read the letter and write a suitable reply using the guidelines which follow it.

Useful language

Beginning the letter
Thank you for your order of (date).

Prices
We can quote you a price of 150 Euros per unit CIF / FOB / CF Hamburg.

Delivery
We can deliver by 5 June.
We can deliver within one month.
We can guarantee delivery within one week of receipt of your order.
We can ship as soon as we receive your order.

Discounts
We can offer a discount of 5% on orders over £1,000.

Payment
We require payment by bank transfer.
We would like payment by letter of credit at sight / 30 days / 60 days.
We wish to be paid by bill of exchange.

Ending the letter
We hope you find our quotation satisfactory and look forward to receiving your order.
Thank you once again for your enquiry.
If you need any further information, please contact us.

TRENDSETTERS
150 East 70th Street • New York • NY 10021 • USA

Mr C. Ling
Fortune Garment Company (Head Office)
Swire House
Connaught Road
Central
Hong Kong

25 October

Dear Mr Ling

Our ref: Order DL137

Following our recent telephone conversation, I would like to confirm our order (No. DL137) for the following:

2,000 Jackie Chen brand silk ties (catalogue number R192) in the following quantities:
    500 design JC1
    500 design JC2
    400 design JC4
    300 design JC5
    300 design JC7

We would expect our normal 10% discount off list price for this bulk order.

If you do not have the items requested in stock, please advise us immediately. The goods should be sent air freight as they are urgently required for our winter sale.

Payment will be made on receipt of goods. We would appreciate delivery by the end of November and look forward to your acknowledgement.

Yours sincerely,

Peter Gilmartin

Peter Gilmartin
Chief Buyer

Guidelines

1 Acknowledge the letter.
2 Thank them for their order.
3 Agree to the normal 10% discount.
4 Advise that design JC1 is out of stock because of great demand and will not be in stock until after Christmas.
5 Offer a close substitute, JC9, which is a similar design although a different colour, with 5% additional discount on that line.
6 Remind them that payment must be made in US dollars.
7 End on an optimistic note.

Brands

A Match these common business English words and phrases with the definitions.

1 cash cow   **a)** to try to increase the sales or popularity of a product, for example by special advertising

2 loss leader   **b)** a profitable product or business generating a steady flow of sales revenue

3 market share   **c)** expensive compared to other products of the same type

4 niche   **d)** the proportion of sales that a company or product has in a particular market

5 promote   **e)** a part of a larger market

6 saturate   **f)** a product sold unprofitably in order to attract customers who will then buy profitable products

7 sector   **g)** a special area of a market which has its own particular customers and requirements

8 upmarket   **h)** to fill the market so completely that no more products can be added

B Here is an extract from a marketing plan for *Caribcool International*, a soft drinks company. Complete the report with some of the words from the list above.

Marketing plan

Positioning

We need to strongly promote a) our .cash.cow.........¹, *Gogo*, which we are relaunching and which still brings in the majority of our revenue and b) our new sports drink, *Fizz Up*. We feel we have found a new market ....². This expensive, ...³ product should be very successful if we ....⁴ it effectively.

Competition

In soft drinks our ....⁵ remains stable at 5%. However, competition is fierce and one of our main rivals is selling its exclusive brand as a ....⁶. They are doing this in order to persuade consumers to switch loyalty to their brands, even though they will lose money in the short term.

C Match the following words to their abbreviations.

> ~~development~~ development ~~new~~ of opportunities point
> point (proposition) ~~product~~ public relations research sale
> selling strengths threats unique weaknesses

1 NPD *New product development* ....
2 USP ....
3 POS ....
4 PR ....
5 R & D ....
6 SWOT ....

D Complete the following table with appropriate forms of the words.

Noun (thing)	Noun (person)	Verb
competition	*competitor*	*compete*
	distributor	
		promote
		research
	consumer	
		advertise

E Complete the following sentences using a form of the word *competition*.
1 There is a lot of .... among coffee producers at present.
2 *Caferoma*'s main .... is *Nescafé*.
3 *Caferoma* needs to .... at home and abroad.

F All the words in the box form partnerships with the word *market*. Decide if each word goes before or after *market* and enter it in the table. (One word goes both before and after.)

> ~~developing~~ domestic down established expanding forces
> leader mass new niche overseas place price research
> sector share shrinking survey up

............*developing*............   ....
....
....
....
....
MARKET
....
....
....
....
....

Language review
Past simple and present perfect

A Peter Fisher is *Caferoma*'s Head of Sales. He is introducing himself and the company to new sales recruits. Complete his speech with the past simple or present perfect forms of the verbs in brackets.

Good morning and congratulations on becoming a member of *Caferoma*'s successful sales team. I'm Peter Fisher, Head of Sales. First I'll introduce myself and then I'll tell you a little bit about your new company.

I *left* ....[1] (leave) university 20 years ago and then I ....[2] (go) to the United States. I ....[3] (join) *Caferoma* 15 years ago and ....[4] (work) in the Sales Department for 10 years. I ....[5] (become) Head of Sales last July and I ....[6] (not have) a holiday since then.

Caferoma ....[7] (be) the market leader for many years now. A year ago we ....[8] (reorganise) our Sales Department and, since November, our turnover ....[9] (increase) by 12% and our share price ....[10] (rise) sharply because of our excellent results. In the last three months we ....[11] (cut) costs by almost 5%.

Bringing us up to date, last week *Caferoma* ....[12] (launch) an advertising campaign for a low-priced decaffeinated product. It will be your first job to sell this product.

B Read this fax sent by Nathalie Druot, a sales representative in France for *Caribcool International*. Complete the fax with the correct form of the verbs in brackets.

Fax message

Caribcool International

20 Rue de Pontoise
Paris 75005
France
Telephone: + 33 1 92 08 56 67
Fax: + 33 1 92 08 56 68

To: Marten Bros.
+ 44 132 1175
Attention: David Black
From: Nathalie Druot
Date: 9 September
Subject: Sales trip

Pages including this: 1

Dear David

I've tried to phone you several times but have been unable to contact you. I know you want to hear about my recent sales trip, so I'm faxing you this short report.

During the trip, I *visited* ....[1] (visit) a number of supermarkets and hypermarkets in southern France where I ....[2] (give) presentations of our new products. There ....[3] (be) a great deal of interest in our relaunched cola drink, *Gogo*. I think it'll be a winner over here. In Montpelier and Bordeaux, I ....[4] (meet) the owners of some large retail outlets and ....[5] (inform) them of our new discount policy. So far, no one ....[6] (complain) about the lower discounts we are offering.

Last Saturday, I ....[7] (go) to Montpelier and ....[8] (have) an enjoyable lunch with Martine Roland – one of our best customers. She promised to buy 20 cases of *Gogo*, but I ....[9] (not, receive) an order from her yet. I'll let you know as soon as I hear from her.

In Nimes, I ran into François Duperrier. He ....[10] (have) a difficult time lately. He ....[11] (leave) his last job in May and since then, he ....[12] (be) unemployed. He knows the French market inside out. Maybe he could be our area rep in the South of France. What do you think? As you know, our sales in the South ....[13] (fall) by almost 10% in the last nine months or so. This can't go on. We must do something to improve our performance, and I'm simply not able to cover the whole of France by myself.

Some good news now. Our TV commercial for *Gogo* was shown for the first time last night. This morning several people .... [14] (phone) me, saying how much they liked it. They think it effective – very clever and humorous! The commercial should really boost *Gogo*'s sales and get everyone talking about the drink.

Finally, a word about my August sales report. I .... [15] (just, finish) writing it, so you should get it in a few days' time. Sorry it's a bit late.

Best wishes

Nathalie

Writing
Making recommendations

Read the memo that Mario Cumino, Managing Director of *Caferoma*, writes to Susanna Morelli, *Caferoma* Brand Manager. Then, using the notes she has made, write the memo that Susanna Morelli sends in reply.

CAFEROMA
MEMO

To: Susanna Morelli
From: Mario Cumino
Subject: Caferoma decaffeinated; Premium Blend
Date: 5 September

I have recently received several letters of complaint from customers concerning our new decaffeinated product. It seems that they cannot find the product when they look for it on the supermarket shelves. Since we are testing it in these cities, I cannot understand what the problem is. Please look into the matter and let me have your thoughts as soon as possible.

I would also like to know what action you have taken to improve sales of our Premium Blend brand. I am very concerned about the situation as this has been our best selling product for many years.

NOTES FOR REPLY

Decaffeinated Product
Available in all supermarkets, but put on bottom shelves! Supermarkets make more money from their own brands.
Letter of complaint won't be effective. Better to offer managers cash to display our products properly.

Improving Premium Blend Sales
Not easy to increase sales. Price is too high. Packaging looks old-fashioned.
Changes needed: Price reduction; new packet design; new advertising campaign focusing on the brand's qualities, image, etc.; special promotions, e.g. tasting sessions in big stores.

Vocabulary

A Match the sentences below to the situations in the photos.

a) At an airline check-in counter

b) On a plane

c) At reception in a hotel

d) In a restaurant

e) At a railway station

f) At car hire firm

1	Which bus will take me downtown?	....c....
2	Could I have the bill / check please?	....
3	How long will you be staying?	....
4	What did you have from the mini-bar?	....
5	Is this self-service?	....
6	I'd like an aisle seat at the back.	....
7	Did you pack the case yourself?	....
8	When does the express to Montreal leave?	....
9	Your baggage is 5 kilos overweight. You'll have to pay excess.	....
10	It's $1,000 for three days. Unlimited mileage.	....
11	Is it automatic or manual?	....
12	On the left, you can see the Adriatic coast.	....
13	There may be turbulence over the Himalayas.	....
14	I'd like a round trip to Chicago.	....
15	Here's your boarding pass.	....
16	We'll be landing in 25 minutes.	....
17	Is this your hand luggage?	....
18	This dish is quite spicy.	....
19	Please return to your seats and fasten your safety belts.	....
20	Smoking is forbidden in the toilets.	....

B Complete the following table with appropriate forms of the words.

Verb	Noun (thing)	Noun (person)
commute	*commuting*	*commuter*
immigrate		
travel		
tour		
visit		

C Put the words in the box under the appropriate headings. You may put some words in more than one column.

breakdown   check-in   disembark   gate   platform   runway
rush hour   sleeper   surcharge   tailback   terminal   traffic-jam
turbulence   upgrade

Land	Sea	Air
breakdown		

Language review

Will

Complete the text by choosing the most appropriate phrase from below.

Airports ....a...........[1] to capacity next year. If you are not delayed at check-in, air-traffic control ....[2] you. In the next three years alone the number of people passing through airport terminals ....[3] by 270 million.

Airport terminals ....[4] more commercial. Airports ....[5]. Increased use of smart cards and electronic tickets are easing the pressure on terminals by cutting queues. More airlines ....[6] Cathay Pacific in creating downtown check-in facilities. Before long, luggage deliveries ....[7] by the incorporation of microchips in suitcases.

From *Fear of Flying*, The World in 1998, *The Economist*

1   **a)** will be packed   **b)** will pack   **c)** will be packing

2   **a)** will be getting   **b)** will get   **c)** will be gotten

3   **a)** will be rising   **b)** will rise   **c)** will be risen

4   **a)** will be becoming   **b)** will become   **c)** will have become

5   **a)** will be speeding up   **b)** will be speeded up   **c)** will have been speeded up

6   **a)** will follow   **b)** will be followed   **c)** will have followed

7   **a)** will improve   **b)** will be improving   **c)** will be improved

Language work

Writing
Replying to letters of complaint

A **Silvina Pietragalli recently flew home to Argentina. She had a very unpleasant flight and she wrote to Alpha Airlines to complain about it.**

These are the points she mentioned in her letter:

- a group of young people were behaving badly
- they were drinking alcohol and being very noisy
- they were moving around the plane disturbing other passengers
- passengers were unable to relax or sleep
- the cabin crew were unable to deal with the situation
- the situation not only unpleasant but dangerous
- Ms Pietragalli is unlikely to fly with Alpha Airlines again

The following reply was sent to Ms Pietragalli by Alpha's Customer Relations Manager. Complete the letter with suitable words or phrases from the box.

compensate	~~concerned~~	the difficulties you encountered	in the future
inconvenience	looked into	once again	sincere apologies
	to my attention	to offer you	unfortunately

Alpha Airlines · 1758 Center Street · Los Angeles · CA 90027 · USA

Ms. Silvina Pietragalli
Av Mansilla 15
08034 Buenos Aires
Argentina

December 15

Dear Ms. Pietragalli:

Thank you for your letter of December 10. I was extremely _concerned_ ....[1] to learn about the unpleasant experience you had during your flight to Argentina. I would like to apologize on behalf of Alpha Airlines for the annoyance and ....[2] you suffered.

I have ....[3] the matter and talked to the staff concerned. They agreed that the young people were noisy and some of them did drink too much. However, they said that these passengers seemed to be having a good time and the staff didn't want to 'spoil their fun'. I showed them your letter and explained how upset you were. They now regret that they did not take action to control the situation. They wish to offer you their ....[4]. I should add that the flight attendants in question had only recently finished their training and therefore were rather inexperienced. ....[5], they were not used to dealing with this kind of situation. I am sure that they will learn from the incident and know how to deal with such behavior in future.

I hope that the 'bad memories' of the flight will soon disappear. To ....[6] for the inconvenience caused to you, I would like ....[7] a gift from our catalogue. Please choose one of the items displayed in the catalogue on pages 6–10. Let us know your selection and we shall send you the gift without delay. ....[8], please accept our apologies for ....[9]. Thank you very much for bringing this matter ....[10]. I very much hope that you will continue to use our airline when you travel ....[11].

Yours sincerely,

Lisa Kaplan

Lisa Kaplan
Customer Relations Manager

B Put the following points in order to show how Lisa Kaplan's letter is organised.

☐ describe what action has been taken

☐ offer some kind of compensation

☐ apologise

☑ *1* refer to the letter received

☐ show understanding and sympathy

☐ apologise again

C Write a suitable letter to deal with one of these situations. Invent an address for the people and companies concerned. Use some of the expressions from the Useful language box.

1 A customer complains that a machine made by your company has broken down several times.

2 An official of a national Health Authority is angry because deliveries of drugs from your company arrived a month late. The drugs were needed urgently.

3 A company buyer refuses to accept a shipment of personalised pens sent by your company because the company's name has been misspelt on each pen.

4 An accounts manager writes to you about errors in a sales invoice you sent to them concerning the sale of 20 tables and chairs. They were billed for $40,800. The correct amount is $4,800.

Useful language

Showing understanding and sympathy

I am very sorry to hear that ...
I am sorry that you were dissatisfied with ...

Apologising

I would like to apologise for the inconvenience you suffered.
the problems you experienced.
Please accept our sincere apologies.

Indicating action

I have looked into the matter.
I have checked with the staff involved.

Offering compensation

To compensate you for the inconvenience, we would like to offer you ...

Ending the letter

Thank you for bringing this matter to my attention.
Once again, my apologies for the inconvenience caused.
We very much regret the embarrassment / annoyance you experienced.
I very much hope that you will continue to use our company in the future.

Language work

4 Advertising

Vocabulary Ⓐ **Complete the text with the words below.**

> adding   capturing   differentiating   ~~gaining~~   giving
> helping   opening

> Advertising does not work in the same way as a sales pitch. Very little advertising tries to persuade anyone to buy immediately. Advertising has to motivate customers to take further action, such as making a telephone call or visiting the shops.
>
> Creative advertising offers many benefits and helps businesses to meet their objectives by:
> 1 _Gaining_........ the attention of the audience.
> 2 .... their imagination.
> 3 .... their minds to your sales messages.
> 4 .... your products and services from all others.
> 5 .... them a reason to choose you.
> 6 .... value to your products and services.
> 7 .... the audience to remember your products / services.

Ⓑ **Complete the questions with the best word or expression.**

1 Who are our existing ..._customers_.........................?
   a) customers   **b)** consumers   **c)** customs

2 Where are they ....?
   a) standing   **b)** located   **c)** staying

3 How do we .... with them at present?
   a) communicate   **b)** reach   **c)** attract

4 What is our unique selling ....?
   a) idea   **b)** thing   **c)** point

5 Who and where are our .... customers?
   a) potential   **b)** desired   **c)** hopeful

6 How can we .... them through advertising?
   a) focus   **b)** reach   **c)** get

7 What do we know about our ....?
   a) opponents   **b)** opposites   **c)** competitors

8 How is our .... of products / services different from theirs?
   a) range   **b)** size   **c)** scope

9 What are their ....?
   a) ups and downs   **b)** strengths and weaknesses   **c)** give and take

10 How do they advertise? What .... do they use?
   a) media   **b)** routes   **c)** canals

Language review
Articles

A Complete the following extract with *a*, *an*, *the* or – (no article).

Sun Advertising, ...*the*........¹ Japanese advertising agency, has beaten its main competitor ....² *Top Ad*, to win ....³ contract to promote ....⁴ *Tora*'s new soft drinks range. They are going to launch ....⁵ 10-billion yen TV advertising campaign – one of ....⁶ biggest ever seen in ....⁷ Japan. ....⁸ campaign includes ....⁹ ad with ....¹⁰ best baseball player from every major baseball team in ....¹¹ Japan. ....¹² Tatsuo Tokunaga, ...¹³ director who dreams up ....¹⁴ *Sun Advertising*'s campaigns, says that ....¹⁵ firm tries to capture people's attention.

B Put the following words into the correct categories in the chart.

Africa   Asia   Baltic Sea   Brazil   Broadway   Channel Islands   China   Far East   Hilton   Holiday Inn   India   London   Middle East   Netherlands   New York   Oxfordshire   Pennsylvania Avenue   Philippines   Punjab   Ritz   Sahara   Texas   Thames   United Kingdom   United States of America   Vancouver   West Indies

No article	The
Continents and most countries *Africa, Brazil*	Countries whose name includes unions or plurals
States and counties	Geographical features and most geographical regions
Towns and cities	Island groups
Most streets	Hotels

C Correct the mistakes in the use of articles in the following text.

'What's *the* best advert you've ever seen?'

'Well, I remember I was reading newspaper in Holiday Inn near Heathrow airport. I had just returned to United Kingdom from a marketing trip to the New York. I'd been staying in the Ritz. Anyway the newspaper – I think it was *Financial Times* – had an article about what was a best advert of the century. I think one of *Marlboro*'s cigarette adverts was voted a best. However I have always liked the *Coca Cola*'s adverts. I think it would be interesting to look at what adverts are popular in different cultures. Would an advert that was popular in the United States also be popular in the Africa or the Asia?'

Writing
Making complaints

A Jonathan Webb, Marketing Director of *Executive Golfing Ltd*, placed an order for an advertisement with an agency. On 15 May he stated the following requirements to Rachel Levy at RL Media:

- Publication: *Ambition* magazine
- Last date for submission of text: 10 June
- Issue date: 27 June
- Position: as specified – no alternative position accepted
- Payment: on last day of month following publication
- Advertisement to be approved before publication

It is now 5 July. Jonathan Webb has just received a copy of the latest issue of *Ambition* magazine with the advertisement in it. He has noticed that the advertisement did not appear as requested.

Read the letter that he sends to Rachel Levy, pointing out the mistakes and refusing to pay the agreed price. Choose the appropriate expression for each space.

Rachel Levy
RL Media
West View Rd
London
W1 6PL

Executive Golfing Ltd

25 Holland Park Avenue
London
W11 2KL

5 July

Dear Rachel,

I have [1] (just received / ~~just got~~) the latest issue of your magazine and checked our advertisement. I'm [2] (unhappy / sorry) to tell you that a number of mistakes have been made by RL Media. I wrote to you on 15 May [3] (confirming / saying) the details of the advertisement. [4] (Unfortunately / And) the following mistakes have [5] (come up / occurred):

- The advertisement appeared in the issue of 4 July instead of 27 June.
- It was on a left-hand page instead of a right-hand page.
- It was placed in the last part of the magazine. We [6] (said / specified) that it should be in the front part.

We [7] (said strongly / made it clear) that the correct position of the advertisement was [8] (absolutely vital / the most important thing). As you can imagine, the incorrect placing of the advertisement has caused us great [9] (trouble / inconvenience) and will no doubt [10] (affect / hurt) sales of our new product range. Due to all these errors, we [11] (don't want to/ feel unable to) pay the full cost of the advertisement. I am, however, prepared to pay 40% of the cost and trust that you [12] (like the idea / consider this acceptable).

I look forward to [13] (receiving / hearing) your comments [14] (as soon as possible / quickly).

Yours sincerely

Jonathan Webb

Jonathan Webb
Marketing Director

B **Reorder the following, so that they show the usual structure of a letter of complaint.**

☐ Explain what went wrong or why you were dissatisfied.

☐ End with an appropriate comment.

☐ Mention the inconvenience caused.

☐ *1* Begin by regretting the need to complain.

☐ Suggest how the matter can be put right or what your solution to the problem is.

Now look at Jonathan Webb's letter and check how he organises his ideas.

C **Study the expressions in the Useful language box, then choose one of the situations below and write a letter of complaint.**

> **Useful language**
>
> **Opening the letter**
>
> I am writing to complain about ...
> I am sorry to tell you that ...
> I am writing with reference to ...
>
> **Explaining why you are dissatisfied**
>
> There seems to have been an error.
> There appears to be a mistake / a misunderstanding.
>
> **Requesting action**
>
> I would be glad if you would look into the matter.
>
> **Suggesting action**
>
> The best solution would be to ...
> I'd like to suggest that ...

1 You recently saw a television commercial promoting a new computer game, *Death Mission 2*. It featured scenes of extreme and graphic violence. It was shown at 6 o'clock in the evening and was aimed at children. You think the game is unsuitable for children because it makes violence look attractive. Write to the television company explaining why the commercial should not be shown.

2 Write your own letter of complaint, for example, about a poor product or unsatisfactory service that you have experienced.

Employment

Vocabulary

A **Read the definitions. Then put the anagrams in the correct order. The first letter of each word is in bold.**

1 To give someone a more important job and more money.

metproo ...*promote*........

2 Three words related to losing a job.

reif ....

ca**s**k ....

smi**d**sis ....

3 Two words for people being considered for a position.

nid**c**ateda ....

plact**a**pin ....

4 To fill in a form or write a letter for a job.

lyp**a**p ....

5 To find new workers to join a company.

crutrie ....

6 On time.

putuclan ....

7 A person who has other people working for them.

le**p**eromy ....

8 Clever and skilful at understanding situations and behaviour.

ut**a**tes ....

9 To stop doing a job because of age.

terrie ....

B **Match the verbs with appropriate nouns in the table below. Sometimes there is more than one possibility.**

	an application form	a covering letter	a CV / résumé	an interview	new staff	a post	a probationary period	a reference	a short-list	a vacancy
to advertise						✔				✔
to attend										
to complete										
to draw up										
to fill in / out										
to hire										
to submit										
to supply										
to write										

**Language review
Questions**

A Use the words to make questions about Mark and his working life.

1 What / Mark / do / for a living?   *What does Mark do for a living?*
He's a sales representative.

2 Where / Mark /work?   ....
In London.

3 When / he / start / work there?   ....
6 months ago.

4 He / enjoy / his job?   ....
Yes.

5 What / he / do / spare time?   ....
He plays golf.

6 How much / he / earn?   ....
£50,000 a year.

7 He / have / any perks?   ....
Yes, a company car.

8 He / get / a bonus?   ....
Yes, twice a year.

9 Why / he / leave / his last job?   ....
Because he was fired.

10 What / he / do?   ....
He hit a colleague.

B Miyuki Kimura is introducing herself at a training session. Read the text below, then write questions for the answers.

Hello everybody. I'm Miyuki Kimura and I'm an analyst for a Swiss securities company in Tokyo. I've been working there for three years. I was born in Yokohama in 1962 and I travel to work by train. It takes one and a half hours. In my spare time I play golf and tennis.

I left my last company because it was difficult for a woman to be promoted. The thing that interests me most in my current job is the opportunity to work with some of the top analysts in Japan. My colleagues say I'm a good team member.

1 *What's your name?* ....   Miyuki Kimura.

2 ....   I'm an analyst for a Swiss securities company.

3 ....   For three years.

4 ....   In Yokohama.

5 ....   By train.

6 ....   One and a half hours.

7 ....   Golf and tennis.

8 ....   Because it was difficult for a woman to be promoted.

9 ....   The opportunity to work with some of the best analysts in Japan.

10 ....   I'm a good team member.

Writing
Giving news to job applicants

A **Read this letter making an offer of employment. Then decide whether the statements below are true or false.**

1 Mr Wills will start work immediately. `F`

2 He will receive one month's salary on his first day at work. ☐

3 His salary will be reviewed after six months. ☐

4 His deputy will be Robert Stephens Jr. ☐

5 He is allowed to join the company pension plan. ☐

6 His working hours will be decided after discussion with Slim Gym's management. ☐

7 He has to work a minimum of three months before leaving the company. ☐

8 Lyn Ashley expects him to telephone her to accept the job. ☐

Mr. Bob Wills
5 York St.
Greenwich Village
New York
NY 10011

August 26

RE: General Manager vacancy

Dear Mr. Wills,

Following your interview for the above position on August 24, I am delighted to confirm our offer of the job, starting on January 1.

Your salary will be paid monthly in arrears. It will be reviewed annually in July. You will report to Robert Stephens, Jr., Managing Director. Our normal terms of employment are enclosed with this letter. We have a company pension plan which you will be eligible to join.

Your working hours each week will include some evenings and weekends, to be determined by mutual agreement. You will be entitled to ten days' annual vacation in addition to public holidays.

One month's notice is required on either side to terminate the contract. There will be a probationary period of three months. Should you decide to accept the offer, please sign the enclosed copy of the contract and return it to me as soon as possible.

I look forward to hearing from you in the near future.

Yours sincerely,

Lyn Ashley

Lyn Ashley
Personnel Director, Slim Gyms

88 Harvey Place 11–C
New York
NY 10003–1324

Language work

B The draft letter below is addressed to an unsuccessful candidate for the vacancy at *Slim Gyms*. Put a circle around any language that you think is too informal for the situation.

> Dear (Michael,)
>
> After our chat about the job, it's a pity but you didn't get it this time. On the day, the other people were better. The guys thought your résumé and interview were fantastic, but you hadn't done enough for this job.
>
> Anyway, now is a good time to say thanks for coming to Slim Gyms and we hope you find a job soon and have a good life.
>
> Best wishes

C Complete this corrected version of the draft letter using items from the box.

candidates	experience	high	impressed	inform	~~Mr. Bolen~~
position	sincerely	success	take	thank	unsuccessful
		wish	would		

RE: General Manager vacancy

Dear _Mr. Bolen_ [1],

Following your interview for the above position on August 25, I regret to .... [2] you that you were .... [3] on this occasion. The standard of .... [4] was extremely .... [5], and while the panel were very .... [6] with your résumé and interview, it was felt that you did not have the necessary .... [7] for the .... [8].

However, I .... [9] like to .... [10] this opportunity to .... [11] you for your interest in Slim Gyms and to .... [12] you every .... [13] in your future career.

Yours .... [14],

D Now underline the phrases in the letters in exercises A and C which give good and bad news to candidates.

Language work

Vocabulary

A Match the following abbreviations to the definitions.

1 CF
(cost and freight)

2 CIF
(cost, insurance
and freight)

3 ex-works
(or ex-factory)

4 FAS
(free alongside
ship) or *franco quay*

5 FOB
(free on board)

a) The price excludes all delivery charges. The buyer has to arrange for collection of the goods at the works or factory, and pays all expenses such as loading, insurance and carriage.

b) The seller's price includes all charges and risks up to the point where the goods are placed alongside the named ship ready to be taken on board.

c) The seller's price includes all charges and risks up to the point where the ship carrying the goods arrives at the named port of destination.

d) The price paid to the seller includes packing and freight to the port of destination, but does not include insurance. This must be paid by the buyer.

e) The seller's price includes all charges and risks up to the point where the seller delivers the goods on board at the named port of shipment. From that point, the buyer bears the charges and risks.

B A buyer has been quoted £2,000 for 100 leather jackets. Look at the five types of quote above. Which type represents the best value to the buyer? Put them in order.

1 (Best value) *CIF* ....   4 ....

2 ....   5 (Worst value) ....

3 ....

C Put the following vocabulary items in the correct box.

air freight   barrels   ~~bill of exchange~~   certificate of value and origin   containers
crates   customs officer   docks   drums   freight forwarding agent   import duty   import licence
insurance broker   insurance premium   letter of credit   port of arrival   port of origin   rail freight
sacks   sales invoice   sea freight   surcharge   warehouse

1 Documents	2 Means of transport	3 Packaging	4 Payments	5 People	6 Places
bill of exchange					

Language review
Conditions

A **Choose the correct alternative to complete these sentences.**

1 We will agree to sign the new contract (provided that / ~~unless~~) you increase our salaries by 5%.

2 We will sign the deal tomorrow (unless / as long as) something goes wrong.

3 (Provided that / Unless) we hear from you by 5 pm tomorrow, we will assume that the deal is off.

4 I won't accept the overseas posting (unless / so long as) I can have my job back when I return.

5 We should be able to avoid a strike tomorrow (unless / provided that) we agree to all the union's demands.

6 (Unless / So long as) we continue to order over 500 cases, they will continue giving us free delivery.

7 (Provided that / Unless) we discuss the matter now, the problem is going to get worse.

8 We will be able to commence work (as long as / unless) the deposit is paid.

9 We will sign this contract tomorrow (unless / provided that) there are no further problems.

10 John was prepared to come to the meeting (unless / provided that) he could bring his union representative.

B **Look at this negotiation between Leslie Palmer, Export Sales Manager, and Michael Mrozek, who will be an agent for Leslie Palmer's company. Complete the dialogue with appropriate words.**

Leslie   Michael, I'm calling from my office and have to go into a meeting in ten minutes. Can we get straight down to business?

Michael   Certainly – go ahead.

Leslie   There are two or three points concerning the contract. Most important, the question of exclusivity. We've reconsidered our position, you'll be pleased to hear. We're ready to offer you exclusivity. If we _make_ ....[1] you an exclusive agent, however, we ....[2] you to pay all advertising and promotion costs. How do you feel about that?

Michael   Yes, I think we can agree to that. Exclusivity is very important for us.

Leslie   Fine, OK then. Another point: the length of the contract. We're willing to offer a three-year contract as long as you ....[3] our sales targets. They're very reasonable, as you know. If you fail to ....[4] our target in any year, we ....[5] the right to renegotiate the contract.

Michael   I can't see any problem there. We're confident we can exceed the targets you set.

Leslie   Good. Let's talk about commission. We are ....[6] to offer you an extra commission – 5% more – provided that you ....[7] responsibility for chasing any unpaid invoices sent to customers.

Michael   You want us to get the money from slow-paying customers?

Leslie   Yes. We don't want the hassle of chasing after bad debts.

Michael   Hmm... an extra 5% for the extra work. That sounds ....[8]. OK, I can agree to that.

Leslie   Good – I'll send you a letter confirming these points.

Writing
Placing an order

A Complete this extract from a fax with words from the box.

alternative	at sight	cases	consignment	delivery	~~following~~
	settle	shipping documents	warehouse		

FAX

☰ D VINCENT Plc ☰

80 Selbourne Road
Sheffield
S10 4AD
Telephone: +44 1472 298590
Fax: +44 1472 135208
E-mail: michael.williams@vincent.com

If you do not receive all the pages, please let us know as soon as possible.

To: Sales Department, Allparts Ltd
From: Michael Williams, Purchasing Department
Date: 16 June
Subject: Our order no. PX305

Number of pages: 2

Dear Sir / Madam,

On the *following*..........[1] page please find our order No. PX305 for various car accessories and motor cycle covers in different colours and designs.

We agreed that the ....[2] will be sent by sea. The covers will be individually wrapped and packed in ....[3], then transported by container ship.

.....................[4] of the goods will be within four weeks, to our ....[5] in Manchester. We reserve the right to refuse goods delivered after that time.

The prices quoted in your catalogue are CIF Dover. We will pay by irrevocable letter of credit ....[6]. Would you please send copies of the ....[7] and your invoice direct to me.

When I spoke to you last week, you agreed that for future transactions, you might allow us to ....[8] quarterly.

If any of the goods ordered are not available, we are willing to accept ....[9] colours or designs.

B The order form on the next page and a covering fax will be sent to Johan Guertler, Sales Manager of *G. Steiner Gmbh*. Write the covering fax according to the guidelines, using some of the phrases from the Useful language box. Sign the fax with your own name.

Order No. RD 8150

Quantity	Item	Code	Unit price	Total cost
80	Silver car covers	CC18	€ 200	€ 16,000
50	Red motor cycle covers	CM21	€ 200	€ 10,000
20	Roof racks	RKS10	€ 250	€ 5,000
			Gross Total	€ 31,000
			Discount @ 5%	€ 1,550
			Net amount due	€ 29,450

Prices are quoted CIF Heathrow airport.
Terms: Payment on presentation of shipping documents.

Guidelines

Your fax should mention the following:
- You are sending an order form with the fax.
- You expect delivery within four weeks, at the latest. You will not receive the goods after this date.
- The goods must be carefully packed in crates and shipped by air freight to Heathrow airport.
- You will pay by banker's draft as soon as they send the shipping documents.
- You will accept alternative models for the roof racks, but not for the car or motor cycle covers. Make this point very clear.
- Ask them to send an up-to-date catalogue and price list.
- Ask if the discount is correct. You were hoping for a trade discount of at least 10%.

Useful language

Beginning the letter / fax
Please find enclosed our order No. .....

Packing
The goods should be packed in cases / crates / containers ...

Transport
Please send the goods by air / sea / road / rail freight.

Delivery
The goods must be delivered by 25 May at the latest.
Delivery must be within four weeks.
Please confirm your delivery date.

Discounts
Thank you for offering a trade discount of 15% and a quantity discount of 5% for orders over 750 units.
We feel that your discount of 3% is rather low.

Payment
We agree to pay by bank transfer / bill of exchange.
Payment will be by letter of credit at sight / 30 days / 60 days.

Closing the letter
We look forward to doing business with you in the future.

Innovation

Vocabulary

Match the verbs with appropriate nouns in the table below. Sometimes there is more than one possibility.

	designs	ideas	problems	research	solutions	tests
analyse		✔	✔			
brainstorm						
carry out						
come up with						
conduct						
develop						
do						
find		.				
patent						
solve						
tackle						

Language review
Passives

A Rewrite the following sentences to make the words in italics the subject of the sentence.

1 Jean-Antoine Menier invented *the chocolate bar*.
   The chocolate bar was invented by Jean-Antoine Menier.

2 Abraham Verhoeven invented *the newspaper* in 1605.
   ....

3 We are going to make *20% of our workforce* redundant.
   ....

4 We are relocating *our head office in Canada*.
   ....

5 Carl Benz produced *the first motor car* in 1884.
   ....

6 Patrick Miller built *the first steam ship* in Scotland in 1799.
   ....

7 We were considering *the new proposal* for most of last week.
   ....

8 Ralph Schneider introduced *the credit card* in 1950.
   ....

9 They have cancelled *the 9.00 am flight to Hong Kong*.
   ....

10 They are investigating *the problem*.
   ....

B Make sentences about the origin of these products using the passive (both positive and negative forms) and the verbs given in the box.

assemble	build	distil	find	grow	make
	manufacture	mine	produce		

1 wine   *Wine is made in France. It is not produced in Norway.*

2 coffee ....

3 perfume ....

4 whisky ....

5 Toyota cars ....

6 oil ....

7 cigars ....

8 peanuts ....

9 rice ....

10 ships ....

11 gold ....

C Complete this article with the passive form of the verbs in brackets.

Powdered instant coffee *was devised* ....[1] (devise) by Satori Kato but his idea ....[2] (exploit) by others. The practice of drinking coffee ....[3] (invent) earlier in Arabia where it ....[4] (report) by ar-Razi, an Arab doctor in the 10th century. Coffee ....[5] (produce) in many countries. The coffee bush ....[6] (find) originally in Arabia and Ethiopia, but it ....[7] (now, grow) in Brazil, Colombia, the Ivory Coast, Uganda, Angola, Kenya and Central America. The beans ....[8] (grind) and coffee ....[9] (use) in most countries as a breakfast drink. The first coffee house ....[10] (open) in Paris in 1643 and ....[11] (follow) by others in Oxford (1650) and London (1652).

Coffee bushes produce berries which contain one or two beans. The berries ....[12] (pick) by hand and ....[13] (put) through a pulping machine. The beans which come out ....[14] (place) in large tanks where the pulp ferments. The beans ....[15] (then, wash) and ....[16] (spread out) to dry in the hot sun. After two weeks the beans ....[17] (put) through a machine which removes the last of the skin. It is not until the coffee beans ....[18] (roast) that they get their fragrant scent. After roasting the beans ....[19] (grind) between steel rollers. The best coffee ....[20] (make) from freshly roasted and ground beans.

D Answer each of the following questions using the verbs in brackets.

1 What is happening to Simon? (redundant)
   He is being made redundant. ....

2 What is happening about the marketing department? (relocate)
   ....

3 What happened to the new design? (change)
   ....

4 What has happened to the pound? (devalue)
   ....

5 What has happened to the President? (take ill)
   ....

6 What has happened to the lap-top? (steal)
   ....

7 What has happened to the meeting? (rearrange)
   ....

Writing
Replying to letters of enquiry

A Complete the letter with the following phrases.

| could you also provide | ~~on behalf of~~ |
| place a substantial order | please | the quality of your products |

Pablo Cortez

Avenida Pablo Cortez, no 5 · 35004 Valencia · Spain

Mr C. Davis   5 March
Leatherware plc
14–19 Chatham Place
Manchester M15 4AA

Dear Mr Davis

I visited the Leatherware stand at the Dusseldorf Trade Fair last month
on behalf of ....[1] 'Pablo Cortez' and was impressed by

...................................[2].

...................................[3] send me information about your range

of executive briefcases. I think that these could do well in our market.

...................................[4] full details of prices, delivery dates,

methods of payments and discounts. Could you send all the details in your

letter as we do not have the time to search through large brochures. Also if

you have any other products which might appeal to this segment of the

market, please let me know.

I look forward to hearing from you. If terms and delivery dates are

satisfactory, I hope to ....[5].

Yours sincerely

Pedro Jiminez

Pedro Jiminez

B The following letter is the reply which Colin Davis writes to Pedro Jiminez. There are a number of mistakes in it – sometimes incorrect spelling, sometimes grammatical or usage mistakes. Find the mistakes and write the correct word in the space on the right.

Dear Mr Jiminez

Thank you for your letter of 5 March by enquiring about our rainge of executive briefcases.

The enclosed leeflet summarises the specifications and prices of our total range of brief and attaché cases. In the most cases we are able to suply goods within fourteen days.

We allow a qantity discount of 7% on purchases of 50 or more of models, rising to 15% on quantities of 100 or more. Furthermore we offer a discont of 3% for payment within 14 days from date of invoice. Payment should be paid in sterling and within 30 days.

Finally I have taken you the liberty of enclosing a copy of our latest catalogue giving full detals of our range of executive luggage and leather goods. I hope you will find it of an interest.

Should you have any further questions please do not be hesitate to contact me personally on the above numbers.

We look forward to receive an order from you in the near future.

Yours sincerely

Colin Davis

Colin Davis

1 ......✓..............
2 ......by..............
3 .....range..........
4 ....
5 ....
6 ....
7 ....
8 ....
9 ....
10 ....
11 ....
12 ....
13 ....
14 ....
15 ....
16 ....
17 ....
18 ....
19 ....
20 ....
21 ....
22 ....

C Mr Adriano Gomez, a buyer for a department store in Sao Paulo, Brazil, writes to a clothing manufacturer asking for full details of the company's new range of shirts. He is interested in placing a large order. Write a suitable reply to his enquiry.

8 Organisation

Vocabulary

A Read what four people say about where they work. Then match them to the organograms A–D below.

1 There are a couple of copywriters, account executives, an art director – you know. But there aren't many full-time staff. We use freelancers a lot. The whole thing's run by the three partners. They make all the high-level decisions.

2 Well, I've never met the CEO of the company and, as for the board of directors, I don't even know who they are. I've only met my boss's boss once. I suppose it's very formal, there are rules and regulations for everything. You always know who does what and who's in charge.

3 I go in three afternoons a week to help him with his correspondence and administration. I like it because I love his books. He can be a bit difficult though.

4 There's the boss, and then we're divided into three departments, each with a manager. There's sales, admin and print production – that's where I work.

A	B	C	D
♟	♟♟♟♟♟	♟♟♟	♟
♟ ♟ ♟	♟	♟♟♟♟♟♟	♟
♟♟♟ ♟♟♟ ♟♟♟	♟ ♟ ♟		
	♟♟♟♟♟♟♟		

B Which of the people above works for:

1 an advertising agency?

2 a printing company?

3 a writer?

4 a pharmaceutical company?

C Which of the following words refer to:

a) all the people in a company?

b) people who are in charge of others?

Some words don't belong in either group.

1	assistant	[–]	7	junior	☐
2	boss	[b]	8	personnel	☐
3	chief executive	☐	9	staff	☐
4	deputy	☐	10	supervisor	☐
5	employees	☐	11	workforce	☐
6	foreman	☐			

Language review
Noun combinations

A Match the nouns in each box below to make common noun combinations. You may want to use some of the nouns in the second box more than once.

For example: *business consultant*

	block
	consultant
	department
business	drive
	equipment
management	gurus
	hours
office	leaders
	staff
sales	talk
	tax
	teams
	trip

B Choose the correct or the best phrase in each group.

1 a) the secretary of Mr Lorenzo
   b) Mr Lorenzo's secretary
   c) Mr Lorenzo secretary

2 a) our company future
   b) our companies future
   c) our company's future

3 a) last year's results
   b) last year results
   c) the results of last year

4 a) our sales target
   b) our sale target
   c) our target of sales

5 a) last month board meeting
   b) last month's board meeting
   c) board meeting of last month

6 a) a personnel's policy
   b) a policy of personnel
   c) a personnel policy

7 a) a salary increase
   b) an increase of salary
   c) a salaries increase

8 a) a contract breach
   b) a contract's breach
   c) a breach of contract

9 a) unemployment figures
   b) figures of unemployment
   c) unemployment's figures

Writing
Notices

A The Security Officer at *Rod Engineering* is worried because there have been several thefts from vehicles left in the company car park. Read the memo that he sends to all heads of department.

Memo

To: All heads of department
From: Security Officer
Subject: Thefts from employees' cars
Date: 10 March

Recently several staff have informed me that various articles such as radios, mobile phones and lap-top computers have been stolen from their cars in the company car park. Some cars were broken into but in other cases this was not necessary as the cars had been left unlocked.

We shall be taking action to improve security in the car park. Meanwhile I will send you a notice for the attention of staff. Please ensure it is prominently displayed on your departmental notice board.

Now read the notice the Assistant to the Security Officer prepared.

NOTICE
Stealing at work

A lot of things have been stolen from cars which are parked in the company car park. We are going to take action to stop this. We are thinking of employing a person to guard the car park, but this could be expensive. We are also considering having some kind of surveillance system, e.g. hidden cameras. It will be at least a month before we can take effective action.

You must not be careless. Thieves break into cars if they see things worth stealing. It is a good idea to lock all the doors of your car and don't leave things on the seats. If you see anyone behaving suspiciously, contact your Security Officer, Jim Davis RIGHT AWAY, on extension 204. Don't delay, or else the thief will get away with the stolen articles.

We think it is important to be careful and keep your eyes open. Don't forget, you have a responsibility to protect your car. Don't expect the company to pay if you lose stuff from your car. We also advise you to consider putting a security device in your car. It could save you a lot of money. And think about it, do you really need to drive to work? How about considering other means of travelling? Try to remember the company will not pay for stolen items.

You must obey these instructions. It is your fault if you lose things.

Jim Davis

Note the comments made by the Security Officer and rewrite the notice, improving its layout, language and content.

> *I'm not happy with this notice, Bob – you will have to rewrite it. Here are a few suggestions:*
> - *Layout: You need a better heading. Something more relevant.*
> - *My position, 'Security Officer', should be noted under my name and the notice should be dated.*
> - *The information needs to be presented more clearly and concisely. The points should be in a logical order.*
> - *You need to edit the content of the notice – some information is not relevant.*
> - *Use short sentences to make the key points. Perhaps you could number them or use bullet points.*
> - *Try putting the actions we are taking at the end of the notice.*
> - *Remember, the notice must be easy to read. Don't use words or expressions that are too informal, for example, 'things' (first line).*
> - *The tone isn't quite right.*

B **Use the guidelines below to write a notice to all employees in a company explaining what they should do if there is a fire in the building.**

Guidelines

1 Information should be presented clearly and concisely. Use short sentences.

2 Imperatives and modal verbs are common.

   In case of fire, *close* all windows. *Leave* by the nearest exit.
   Do not collect valuables.
   All visitors *must* report to reception.
   Time sheets *should* be submitted by the end of the week.

3 The tone of the notice should be firm, polite and tactful.

   Please note that goods can only be exchanged or money refunded with proof of purchase.
   <u>Not</u>   Make sure you have a receipt to get your money back.

4 Do not be too informal. Use correct, appropriate language.

   Visitors must report to reception on arrival.
   <u>Not</u>   People must go to the desk when they come in.

5 Useful endings

   Thank you for your co-operation.
   Please contact me if there are any problems.
   We apologise to our customers / staff for any inconvenience caused.

UNIT 9 Money

Language work

Vocabulary

A Write the name of the country next to its currency. Then write the nationality.

Currency	Country	Nationality
dollar	U N I T E D S T A T E S	American
drachma	G _ _ _ _ _	
pound	U _ _ _ _ _ _ _ _ _ _ _ _	
rand	S _ _ _ _ _ _ _ _ _ _	
rouble	R _ _ _ _ _	
won	S _ _ _ _ _ _ _ _ _	
yen	J _ _ _ _	
yuan	C _ _ _ _	

B Write $ in the box provided next to countries which use dollars and £ for those countries that use pounds.

1 Australia $ 4 Egypt ☐   7 New Zealand ☐

2 Canada ☐   5 Hong Kong ☐   8 Singapore ☐

3 Cyprus ☐   6 Lebanon ☐   9 Taiwan ☐

C Are the following statements true or false?

1 o is often read as 'nought' in American English. F

2 o is normally read as 'zero' in American and British English in scientific contexts and for temperatures. ☐

3 James Bond 007 is read as 'double oh seven'. ☐

4 When talking about football results in British English we often say 'Manchester United beat Liverpool seven – zip'. ☐

5 In tennis 30 – 0 is read as 'thirty – love'. ☐

6 In English 50,127 is read as 'fifty point one two seven'. ☐

7 40 is spelt 'fourty'. ☐

8 11.66 is read as 'eleven point sixty-six'. ☐

9 In British English the number 1,999 is read as 'one thousand nine hundred and ninety-nine'. ☐

10 The year 1999 is read as 'nineteen ninety-nine'. ☐

11 The year 2001 is read as 'twenty one'. ☐

12 A billion is 1,000,000,000. ☐

Language review
Trends

A These verbs all describe change. Complete the table with the verb forms and (where possible) the noun form.

Infinitive	Past simple	Past participle	Noun
1 decline	declined	declined	a decline
2 decrease			
3 drop			
4 fall			
5 fluctuate			
6 gain			
7 improve			
8 increase			
9 jump			
10 level off			
11 lose			
12 plummet			
13 recover			
14 rise			
15 rocket			
16 stabilise			

B Tick the type of change expressed by the adverbs in the table.

	Type of change				
	small	large	very large	fast	slow
considerably		✔			
dramatically					
enormously					
gradually					
quickly					
rapidly					
sharply					
significantly					
slightly					
substantially					
vastly					

Grammar note

We use an adjective to modify a noun and an adverb to modify a verb.

For example: *Our share price increased slightly in August.* (verb + adverb)
There was a slight increase in our share price in August. (adjective + noun)

Writing

Organising a report

A **Match the following headings to the correct sections.**

- Conclusion
- Findings
- Procedure
- Recommendations
- Terms of Reference

Report on investment proposal: New magazine

1 ....

This report was commissioned by the Chairman, Manfred Engelmann. It is based on a presentation made by Jane Winter and her associates for a new magazine entitled *Baby*. It was to be submitted by 15 January, together with a recommendation for action.

2 ....

Information for the report was gathered from the following sources:
- CVs of the management team; a business plan; a marketing plan.
- A presentation of the proposal.

3 ....

Baby magazine

a) Description
   Baby is a monthly magazine in English which gives advice to pregnant women and young mothers.

b) Price
   In line with similar magazines, but not less than £3.

c) Target Market
   - Couples about to have their first baby and couples who have just had their first baby. People in upper income groups.
   - People in English-speaking countries, but translation rights to be negotiated.
   - Launch in England and Australia, with the US to follow.

d) Selling Points
   - It fills a gap in the market.
   - It offers helpful advice, serious articles and lighter features on babies and motherhood.
   - Advertisers will be eager to place advertisements because of its well-defined target market.
   - It will be widely distributed through medical centres, hospitals, doctors' waiting rooms, etc.

4 ....

Baby magazine is an excellent project which would be very profitable. It is an original concept which has been well researched by a talented management team.

5 ....

I recommend that we provide the funds requested and proceed to the next stage of development.

Louise Dawson
Director
10 January

B Find words or expressions in the first two sections which mean:

1 asked for
2 developed from
3 given in before
4 as well as a suggestion
5 collected

C Find words or expressions in the last two sections which mean:

1 unique idea
2 carefully investigated
3 continue the project

D Read these sections of a report. They give information about a concept for a new product. Correct the italicised phrases in the report, using more appropriate language.

Introduction

at the request of

I'm writing this report ¹/~~because of~~ the Marketing Director, Stephanie

Marchand. It describes a concept for a new product – a pill for

preventing hangovers – and ² *I've given you some ideas* for developing

and marketing it. The concept resulted from a meeting attended by

members of the R & D and Marketing departments. The report

³ *had to be handed in* by 16 December.

Conclusion

A pill for preventing hangovers would ⁴ *make us a lot of money*. The

R & D department has already ⁵ *made a research* and is certain that an

effective pill could be developed within two years. There is no suitable

pill currently available, so there is clearly a gap in the market.

Recommendations

- The R & D department ⁶ *have got to make* a pill as soon as possible.

- The Marketing department ⁷ *must give us ideas* for packaging and

  marketing the product at the next meeting.

- ⁸ *We have got to know more* about competing products.

Ethics

Vocabulary **A** Match the verbs and nouns in the table below to make word partnerships. Sometimes there is more than one possibility.

	companies	contracts	crimes	documents	laws	products	regulations	sanctions
boycott	✔					✔		
breach								
break								
commit								
falsify								
impose								

B Match the verb to the correct preposition.

accuse		**for** damages
charge		**for** selling dangerous goods
prosecute	somebody	**of** offering bribes
sentence		**to** three years in prison
sue		**with** breaking guidelines

C Match the following prefixes to the verbs to describe some unethical business activities. The number of times that each prefix is used is given in brackets.

For example: *misinform*

de– (1)	book
dis– (1)	charge
mis– (5)	credit
over– (3)	fraud
under– (1)	inform
	lead
	mine
	price
	represent
	treat
	use

Now match the words you have made above to the following nouns.

For example: *misinform consumers*

a company	competitors	confidence	consumers	customers
facts	goods	information	people	seats	staff

D **Choose the correct definition for the italicised words and phrases in these dialogues.**

1 A: Was the company prosecuted for polluting the environment?
   B: Yes, but they were found not guilty because of a *loophole* in the law.

   a) clause   **b)** gap   **c)** case

2 A: How do the high taxes affect people in your country?
   B: Well for one thing there's a growth in the *black economy* and it's worrying the government.

   a) working underground   **b)** night work   **c)** working and not paying tax

3 A: What happened to John?
   B: He was found guilty of *tax evasion* and sent to prison for three years.

   a) not paying enough tax   **b)** paying tax for another person
   c) paying the wrong tax

4 A: What do unethical companies do when they get large amounts of money illegally?
   B: Well, *money laundering* is quite common. It's very hard for the authorities to prove where the money has come from.

   a) investing in property   **b)** keeping money in cash
   c) hiding the origin of money

5 I want durable products, but let's face it – *built-in obsolescence* is typical of most products these days.

   a) very short guarantee   **b)** designed not to last very long
   c) difficult to use

Language review
Narrating

A **Read the story. Then put the events in the order they happened.**

It was 8 o'clock in the evening. Nick was sitting in the bar. He was drinking a beer. He was feeling very guilty because he had lied about feeling sick.

In the morning he had felt really tired and he had phoned the office to say he was sick. His colleague Peter had said that he would work late to cover for Nick. Nick had then gone back to bed. He had got up at 11 o'clock and had had some lunch. He had watched television all afternoon.

Suddenly, Peter was there beside him. Peter looked really angry. Nick apologised and offered to buy Peter a drink. Peter grabbed Nick by the collar of his shirt. Then he just let Nick go and walked out of the bar without saying a word.

a) Nick felt tired.   ☐ *1*

b) Nick offered to buy Peter a drink.   ☐

c) Peter walked out of the bar.   ☐

d) Peter arrived in the bar.   ☐

e) Peter grabbed Nick's collar.   ☐

f) Nick felt guilty.   ☐

g) Nick phoned the office.   ☐

h) Nick watched television.   ☐

i) Nick went back to bed.   ☐

j) Nick went to a bar for a beer.   ☐

B **Complete this story putting the verbs in brackets in the correct form.**

It was 10 o'clock at night. Eddie was tired and hungry. He *had spent* ...... [1] (spend) the last five hours talking to the company's senior managers. He .... [2] (realise) that he would have to resign from his job, and also that he .... [3] (face) the possibility of going to prison.

Six months ago, everything .... [4] (be) fine. He .... [5] (have) a wonderful job and he .... [6] (make) a lot of money. Then he .... [7] (meet) some people who .... [8] (advise) him badly. They .... [9] (give) him a list of companies and .... [10] (tell) him to buy their shares. He .... [11] (use) the company's money to do this. At first the shares .... [12] (rise), so he .... [13] (buy) some more. Everything .... [14] (seem) so easy. Then the stock market .... [15] (crash) and he lost everything.

Eddie .... [16] (telephone) his wife before leaving the office. He .... [17] (apologise) for not phoning earlier, explaining that he .... [18] (have) a difficult meeting. 'You sound upset. Anything wrong?' she asked. 'I'll tell you about it when I get back,' he .... [19] (reply).

A **Read the sales leaflet in which *Paperback Ltd* introduces its services.**

WHY THROW AWAY PAPER? HOW ABOUT GIVING IT TO US?

We are a company with over 20 years' experience of recycling paper. We will collect all the waste paper from your premises, recycle it and save you the cost of disposing of it yourself.

We provide a flexible service designed to meet the needs of environmentally-friendly companies. See our list of satisfied customers and testimonies to our outstanding service (available upon request).

We can help you by:

- saving you time and money
- showing that you care about the environment
- enhancing your image with your customers
- offering you a tailor-made service, with collections at your convenience.

Many people buy only from companies which protect the environment. By using our services, you will show that you TRULY CARE about the environment.

Why not try our one-month trial period, under no obligation? You'll get your money back if you are not fully satisfied. Discounts of up to 20% are available for long-term contracts.

For a friendly, low-cost 'green' service, call us now on 01942 248620 or write to:

Paperback Ltd.
45 Dagenham Road
Oxford
OX6 3DR

We will arrange for one of our representatives to visit you and discuss our service in detail.

GREEN BUSINESS AWARD FOR ENVIRONMENTAL PROTECTION

   PAPERBACK Ltd the company which puts the environment first.

B **Underline the phrases in the text which do the following:**

  1 create interest

  2 describe potential benefits to customers

  3 provide evidence of the company's reputation, level of service and customer satisfaction

  4 encourage customers to take action.

C **Write a sales leaflet persuading new customers to sign a contract in the following situation. Use some of the expressions in the Useful language box. Mention any introductory offers, discounts and other incentives which you think will appeal to potential customers.**

You are Advertising Manager for *Clean Sweep*, an industrial cleaning company which uses green products to clean offices. All its vehicles and equipment are powered by electricity. Its products are environmentally friendly and it uses the latest technology in dust control and efficient cleaning methods. It has a policy of employing people who have been out of work for a long time.

Useful language

Attracting the reader's attention

- use an eye-catching heading.
- ask questions, for example, 'Why throw away paper?'
- make a statement which appeals to the target user.
  'If you are looking for a way of saving money ...'
- give an amazing fact or statistic.
  'Did you know that only 5% of companies benefit from these great savings?'

Describing benefits

You will save time and money by ...
A key feature of our product / service is ...
You will benefit from substantial discounts of up to 15%.
The product is designed to ...

Providing evidence of reputation / service / customer satisfaction

We have over 20 years' experience in this field.
Testimonials from our customers are available upon request.

Encouraging action

For further information, please contact us on the numbers given below.
Please telephone, fax or post the coupon right away.
Phone us FREE quoting the reference number on this leaflet.

Offering incentives

Save up to 5% if you reply before the end of this month.
Accept a free gift when you place your first order.

11 Change

Vocabulary

A The words below are all used in relation to change. Decide whether each word expresses a positive (P) idea or a negative (N) idea.

1 apathy	N	**5** insecurity	☐	**9** progress	☐
2 commitment	P	**6** inspiration	☐	**10** resistance	☐
3 empowerment	☐	**7** loyalty	☐	**11** security	☐
4 inertia	☐	**8** motivation	☐	**12** threat	☐

B Make word partnerships with the following, using some of the words from the list above.

1 company *loyalty* ....

2 job ....

3 .... to change

4 .... of redundancy

5 .... report

C The words below are also used in relation to change.

de-layering	downsizing	insecurity	morale	re-engineering
	relocation	restructuring	team spirit	

1 Which word refers to moving? ....

2 Which three words refer to how people feel?

....

....

3 Which four words refer to a change in structure?

....

....

Language review
Reporting

A Choose an appropriate verb from the box and report what was said in each of the sentences on the next page.

agree emphasise explain point out recommend remind suggest	that ...		advise remind warn	(somebody) to + verb
			recommend suggest	(verb)ing ...
offer promise	to + verb			

1 'We think you are right on this point.'

.*They agreed that he / she was right on that point.*.........................

2 'Be careful of very rapid change.'

....

3 'Don't forget people dislike change.'

....

4 'I'll help you finish the rota.'

....

5 'Why not use a courier service to speed things up?'

....

6 'If I were you I'd speak to the boss first.'

....

7 'It's particularly important to talk about change.'

....

8 'Actually there are several problems with the new location.'

....

9 'The new reporting system works in the following way.'

....

10 'The summer is the best time for you to make these changes.'

....

B **Judith Crede lost her job in recent changes. She went for an interview for a new job with a different company. Afterwards she tells a friend what the interviewer asked her. Write down the actual questions she was asked.**

1 He asked me why I wanted the job.

.*Why do you want the job?*...

2 He wanted to know how long I had been working in my previous job.

....

3 He wanted to know if I could use the latest software.

....

4 He asked me how old I was.

....

5 He wanted to know what I did in my spare time.

....

6 He asked me if I had a clean driving licence.

....

7 He asked me if I spoke any foreign languages.

....

8 He asked me how I felt about all the changes in my previous company.

....

9 He asked me if I smoked.

....

Writing
Agendas and action minutes

A Read the answer phone message below. It was left by Polina Czerny, head of the Polish subsidiary of a multinational company, for her personal assistant Dominic Brown.

Then do the following tasks to prepare the agenda.
- Note down the title, date, time and venue of the meeting.
- Decide on a suitable order for the items to be discussed.
- Think about a suitable wording for each item.

Finally, write the agenda for the meeting.

Dominic, just to let you know I'm flying to Prague after lunch. There are problems at the factory and they want me to help sort things out.

About the agenda for the management meeting on 16 June: I'd like you to prepare it for me please and circulate it as soon as possible. We'll hold the meeting in room 18, next to the boardroom, starting at – let's see … 11 am It must end at 1 pm as I've got to give a talk at the Chamber of Commerce, starting at 2.

There are two important items for the agenda. We must discuss the problem of our agent in Hungary. I'd like to cancel their contract. Not everyone will agree, I know. Michel and Helena are against the idea, so discussion will be lively. I'll need at least 30 minutes for that item. The other big one is reviewing our product range. I'm sure that will take a long time, maybe 45 minutes or even more. Pieter and Ewa want us to reduce our product range, I hear.

Oh yes, we must select two junior executives for the training course at Insead in Paris. Say 10–15 minutes for that. And I'd like to present the proposed designs for our new logo. They're excellent. I don't want to discuss them, just show them to everyone. Fifteen minutes should be enough for that one.

We've got to approve the budget cuts soon, but that could take ages. No one likes cuts, do they? Maybe we should leave this for our next meeting. What do you think? Can we fit it in?

What else? Don't forget 'Any other business' and of course we'll have to fix the time and date of the next meeting. It may take some time because everyone's busy at the moment.

Right, over to you then. Give me a call if you have any problems.

B Read the extracts from a meeting attended by the people below. Then write the action minutes for the meeting using these headings:
- agenda item
- action agreed
- who will do it
- when and how they will report back

Present:

Polina Czerny (chair)	Pieter Koch
Michel Dembrowsky	Susan Lau
Dominic Brown	Lois Marshall

Polina   Right, that didn't take long, I'm pleased to say. We're agreed that Oscar and Rosemarie will attend the Insead seminar. Dominic, I'd like you to call them and tell them the good news. OK?

Dominic   Fine. I'm sure they'll be delighted.

. . .

Polina   Well, it's obvious we can't agree what to do about our Hungarian agent. But we do want to review his performance. Pieter, I know you're busy, but could you go over the figures, call him and hear his side of the story? Then send me a short report on his performance by, say, the end of the month? Can you do that?

Pieter   Certainly. It shouldn't take too long. I'm sure I can manage that.

. . .

Polina   I knew this wouldn't be an easy one. We mustn't do things in too much of a hurry. We all agree, I think, that we'll carry out a study of all our products and identify which ones are unprofitable or not worth spending any money on. Lois, could you do this please? But of course, you'll get plenty of help from marketing.

Lois   Right. How do you want me to report back?

Polina   I don't think we need anything written at this stage. Just report back at our next meeting – that'll do for the moment.

. . .

Polina   I'm very disappointed that you don't like any of the designs for the logos. I just didn't expect you to object so strongly. I suppose we're going to have to start again. It'll be expensive, but OK, we'll ask another firm of design consultants to come up with some ideas for us. Susan, will you prepare a list of, oh, three firms that I could contact? I'd like that on my desk by the end of this week.

Goodness me, it's 1.15. We'll have to end here. I've got to give a talk at the Chamber of Commerce at 2. Looks as if I'll miss lunch. Well, thanks very much everyone. A very lively meeting!

. . .

Language work

Vocabulary

A **Match these verbs and nouns to make common word partnerships.**

1	form	**a)**	an agreement
2	launch	**b)**	an alliance
3	look for	**c)**	a bid
4	penetrate	**d)**	an objective
5	reach	**e)**	a market
6	set	**f)**	a partner
7	take	**g)**	a stake

B **Use the word partnerships above to complete the following sentences.**

1 We have found a company we can *form an alliance* .... with in the Far East.

2 We will never .... for the under-35s unless we change our advertising strategy.

3 By buying up a lot of shares quickly, we were able to .... in one of our competitors before taking them over.

4 The CEO thinks we should .... in Eastern Europe rather than trying to set up our own subsidiary there.

5 After a long and difficult negotiation we were able to ....

6 It took all our financial resources to .... for such a well-known company.

7 At the AGM the Board .... of increasing turnover by 8% in the next two years.

C **Match the halves of each of the following sentences.**

1	A merger has been announced	**a)**	to merge with suitable businesses.
2	They built up a 30% stake in the company	**b)**	so we are looking for foreign partners.
3	We are planning to launch a bid	**c)**	will require new capital investment and could be risky.
4	We are starting an expansion programme	**d)**	and then took it over.
5	We are always looking for opportunities	**e)**	several businesses have been sold off.
6	In order to re-focus the group	**f)**	for our main rival.
7	The MD wants to take the company public	**g)**	between two major oil companies.
8	Diversifying into new sectors	**h)**	to finance an ambitious expansion programme.

Language review
Dependent prepositions

A Tick the preposition that usually follows the verbs in the table. Some of the verbs are not usually followed by a preposition.

	for	on	to	no preposition
account	✔		✔	
agree				
apply				
belong				
complain				
depend				
discuss				
enter				
look				
meet				
pay				
phone				
rely				
talk				
tell				
wait				
write				

B Correct the following sentences.

1 Would you phone ~~to~~ Johnson Consultants regarding the joint venture agreement?

2 I agree that we should enter into the Spanish market by the end of the year.

3 The home market accounts 60% of their sales.

4 We cannot continue to depend for one product.

5 We're relying to your support at the board meeting.

6 We seem to agree the need for an alliance with a German firm.

7 We need to discuss about this further.

8 We are looking on a new partner in Eastern Europe.

9 We'll wait your answer on the take-over proposal.

10 They are complaining the management because they were not consulted about the take-over.

Language work

Writing Reports

A Read the report, then answer the questions.

——— MEMO ———

To: Stephen Wade, Chairman
cc: Peter Evans, Managing Director
From: Yvonne Elliott, Finance Director
Date: 15 March

Report on the proposed merger with Unibank

As requested in your memo of 12 February, here is my report summarising the advantages and disadvantages of a possible merger with Unibank, together with my recommendations. You asked for the report to be submitted by 15 March.

I have collected information from various sources including Unibank's publicity material, annual reports, financial publications and material on the Internet. I also obtained a confidential study of Unibank carried out by City Consultants.

1 Reasons for the merger
  a) Unibank is a well-established and highly respected bank, with over forty branches.
  b) It has a number of important corporate clients, a profitable investment department, a skilled workforce and modern communication systems.
  c) Although at one time it was in financial difficulties, it now seems to have fully recovered.
  d) Unibank is an obvious target for us for a merger. It covers the City of London, an area where we are not well represented, and the merger would allow us to cut costs. Unprofitable branches could be closed down and staffing costs reduced.

2 Reasons against the merger
  a) The unions would strongly oppose staff cuts.
  b) The prospects for growth are not good because of the possibility of a recession.
  c) The management styles of the two banks are very different. Our bank is prepared to take risks to make profits. Unibank, however, is cautious and conservative.
  d) The chairman of Unibank is a strong, charismatic person. He might not be willing to play a secondary role if the merger took place.

3 Recommendations
  a) An in-depth study should be made of Unibank's financial situation.
  b) A meeting should be set up between the chairmen of both banks to discuss the advantages of a merger.
  c) Mergers with other banks in the City should be considered.
  d) It is recommended that a top public relations consultant should be contacted to advise us if the merger goes ahead.

Yvonne Elliot

---

  1 What is the subject of the report?
  2 Who asked for the report?
  3 When was Yvonne Elliott asked to write the report?
  4 What was she asked to do?
  5 When did she have to hand in the report?
  6 How did she get the information?

B Now underline the phrases giving you the information for questions 3–6. These phrases are all helpful when you have to write the introduction to a report.

C Look at the section headed 'Recommendations'. Which grammatical structures are used to make recommendations?

D Write a report for the following situation using expressions from the Useful language box.

You are Site Manager of *Texan Chicken*, a fast-food business. Your General Manager, Edward Thomas, has asked you to write a report on two possible locations in your area for a new restaurant. He telephoned you with his instructions on 10 April, saying, 'Let me know the advantages and disadvantages of each site, and give me a firm recommendation please, with your reasons. Can you let me have the report by 30 April as I have a board meeting the following day?'

	Site A	Site B
Floor space in sq. metres	330	180
Parking	Car park (Maximum 20 cars)	Unrestricted street parking. No car park.
Location	High street. Residential area nearby.	On corner in the city centre.
Building	Ground floor of historic building. A lot of renovation needed.	New building in excellent condition.
Rent per week	£520	£350
Security of area	High crime rate. Shops broken into and vandalised.	Low crime rate because near the police station.
Estimated customer numbers	Now: 1,000 In 5 years: 5,000	Now: 2,000 In 5 years: 3,000

Useful language

Introduction

As requested in your letter / fax / e-mail of 7 June ...
This report was commissioned in response to / in order to ...
The report was to be submitted by 10 July.

Sources

Information was gathered from the following sources:
questionnaires, interviews, personal observation, desk and field research and published reports.

Findings and recommendations

We found that ...
The conclusion we reached was that ...
It is recommended that ...
The company should ...
I suggest that ...

Vocabulary

Tick the two responses that are most appropriate for each of the situations below. Then underline the one that is more formal.

1 You don't hear someone's name when you are introduced to them.
   a) What?
   b) I'm afraid I didn't catch your name.   ✔
   c) <u>Sorry, what did you say your name was again?</u>   ✔

2 You have to refuse an invitation to dinner with a supplier.
   a) Sorry, I can't make it.
   b) I have another appointment.
   c) Unfortunately, I won't be able to come.

3 You accept a dinner invitation.
   a) Yes please.
   b) That sounds great.
   c) Yes, that would be very nice.

4 You invite a business associate for dinner.
   a) Would you like to join me for dinner?
   b) Do you fancy dinner later?
   c) It would be my pleasure to invite you to dinner with me.

5 You greet a visitor you haven't met before.
   a) How do you do?
   b) Nice to meet you.
   c) How are you?

6 You raise your glass to propose a toast.
   a) Here's to our business.
   b) You too.
   c) I'd like to propose a toast.

Language review
Modal verbs

A **Correct the mistakes in the following sentences.**

   1 I would like to ~~can~~ go abroad more.
   2 She must to do it now.
   3 You can have not the cheque now.
   4 I must go into the office last weekend.
   5 I'm sorry to must tell you this.
   6 I don't can type.
   7 Could you telling me the time?

B **A trainer is asking some management trainees to think about business mistakes they have made. First, the trainer gives examples of mistakes by other companies. Write down what the companies should or should not have done.**

   Here are some real mistakes from different aspects of business. I'll start with cultural mistakes, then marketing mistakes and if there is time I'll move on to strategic mistakes.

Right – cultural mistakes. I can't mention company names here for obvious reasons. I'll give you three examples I have heard of this year. Company A served pork to a group of Muslims from Kuwait. Company B lost an important contract in China because they sent a brilliant young negotiator who had just graduated from Harvard Business School with top marks. Company C lost over £1 million in a deal with the Japanese because they started the negotiation by announcing their deadlines. The Japanese then used this deadline to their advantage and the deal was concluded on the way to the airport. The Japanese were always going to agree to the deal, they were just trying to save as much money as possible.

C Now write about a business mistake you made or, if you have never worked, about a mistake. Say what you should or should not have done.

Writing
Invitations and thanking people for hospitality

A Complete the faxed invitation to Don McGill, Marketing Director of an Australian pharmaceutical company. Use the prepositions in the box.

at	for	from	in	on

FAX

PHARMAC INTERNATIONAL INC

Pharmac International, Inc.
3254 Center Street
Staten Island, NY 10308
Tel: +1 212 555 4398
Fax: + 212 555 3876

To: Mr. D. McGill
From: Ingrid Driessen
Date: June 3
Subject: Training session

Number of pages including this one: 1

Dear Mr. McGill:

I was interested to learn *from* ....¹ a colleague that you will be attending the Annual Sales Convention here next month. I understand you plan to stay on ....² New York ....³ a few days after the convention.

We are holding a training seminar ....⁴ members of our department ....⁵ our head office ....⁶ July 5–7. I would like to invite you to lead a half-day session ....⁷ new trends in marketing, preferably ....⁸ July 6. The session could be ....⁹ the morning or afternoon, whichever would be more convenient ....¹⁰ you. I should mention that we can offer you a fee of $250 if you participate ....¹¹ the seminar.

If you are willing to accept this invitation, could you please phone me as soon as possible? We could then discuss the organization of the session ....¹² detail.

I very much hope that you can accept this invitation. It would be an honor ....¹³ our staff to meet you and learn about the latest trends ....¹⁴ marketing.

Yours sincerely,

Ingrid Driessen

Ingrid Driessen
Training Manager

B Read Don McGill's reply and choose the more formal expression in each pair of words or phrases.

FAX

SEGACO

Segaco — A Pharmac Inc company

Segaco
40 Brookhollow Ave
Baulkham Hills
NSW 2153

To: Ms Ingrid Driessen
From: Don McGill
Date: 5 June
Subject: Training session

Number of pages including this one: 1

Dear ¹(*Ingrid* / *Ms Driessen*)

²(*Thanks very much* / *Thank you very much*) for your invitation. I can give the talk ³(*on the date you suggest* / *when you would like*). ⁴(*I would prefer to speak* / *Could I give it*) in the morning as I have another appointment later in the day.

I think I'll be able to give ⁵(*a great talk* / *an excellent presentation*) as I've spoken on the subject many times recently. You ⁶(*mentioned* / *talked about*) a fee of $250 for running the session. ⁷(*This seems rather low* / *This doesn't seem much*) for a three-hour session. Could you reconsider this?

Could you ⁸(*let me have* / *provide me with*) Powerpoint equipment for the talk? ⁹(*One more thing* / *Finally*), ¹⁰(*could you possibly send me* / *can I have*) a few details about the participants?

¹¹(*I'm looking forward to seeing* / *It will be great to see*) you all on 6 July.

¹²(*All the best* / *Yours sincerely*)

Don McGill

Don McGill
Marketing Director

C Write invitations for these situations. Use expressions from the Useful language box.

1 You want to invite someone to give a talk or presentation to members of staff in your company.

2 You have been invited to give the talk / presentation above. Accept or refuse the invitation.

Useful language

Inviting

I would like to invite you to give a talk at our annual dinner.

attend our conference.

visit our factory.

Thanking and accepting

Thank you for the invitation to attend your conference.
I am very pleased to accept your invitation.
The date you suggest is fine.

Refusing an invitation

I am sorry to say that I can't accept your invitation.
Unfortunately I have to be in Boston at that time.

Closing

I look forward to seeing you on 9 December.
I'm sure it will be a very enjoyable day.
Could you please confirm the arrangements by fax / phone / e-mail.

Language work

D When they were in New York, Don McGill and his wife Jenny were entertained by Ingrid Driessen and shown round the city. When Don returned to Australia, he e-mailed Ingrid to thank her for her hospitality. Underline the words and phrases which he uses
a) to express his thanks and
b) to show that he and his wife really enjoyed the visit.

To:	Ingrid Driessen <Ingrid.Driessen@pharmac.com>
From:	Don McGill <McGillD@segaco.com>
Date:	13 July
Re:	New York visit

Dear Ingrid

I want to <u>thank you for your hospitality</u> while I was in New York. It was most kind of you to invite me and Jenny to dinner and to spend time showing us round your city. You helped to make our visit very memorable. Jenny enjoyed immensely visiting some of your famous department stores, and I will never forget the trips to the Empire State Building and Radio City.

If the Annual Sales Convention is ever held in Sydney, I would like to repay you for your generosity and kindness to us.

Please give my best wishes to all your colleagues who attended my seminar. I'm glad everything went well. It was a pleasure to meet you all.

Once again, my thanks for your efforts on our behalf.

Best wishes

Don McGill

E You have recently returned from an overseas sales trip. Write a letter of thanks to the business contact who entertained you during the trip. Refer to the following situations:
- having a meal together at a good restaurant
- arranging your visit to the factory
- taking you to the theatre.

Leadership

Vocabulary

A Match words from each column to make word partnerships which describe activities that leaders are involved in.

1	co-ordinate	**a)**	activities
2	communicate	**b)**	perfomance
3	deal with	**c)**	staff
4	delegate	**d)**	strategies
5	develop	**e)**	tasks
6	issue	**f)**	information
7	measure	**g)**	miracles
8	motivate	**h)**	objectives
9	perform	**i)**	orders
10	set	**j)**	crises
11	take	**k)**	decisions

B Complete the advertisement referring to the word partnerships above.

Aphrodite Cosmetics

Managing Director

As a world leader in the health and beauty sector, Aphrodite is a multinational company with a turnover in excess of £5bn. We are seeking a Managing Director of outstanding calibre to take us into the next decade and beyond.

The Role

The successful candidate will be required to:
- set .*objectives*.[1] and communicate them clearly to staff.
- develop ....[2] which will increase profitability and market share.
- take ....[3] at the highest level affecting both the long and short term activities of the group.
- accurately ....[4] performance both of individuals and departments.
- issue ....[5] which may sometimes be unpopular.

The Person

We are looking for someone who is:
- strong, charismatic and who can ....[6] staff by his / her vision.
- well-organised and who can co-ordinate the ....[7] of the whole group effectively.
- calm when ....[8] a crisis.
- able to ....[9] tasks to others when necessary.
- able to communicate ....[10] clearly and precisely to all levels of the company.

Language review
Relative clauses

A Join these sentences using *who* or *which*.

1 A scientist invented a new drug to treat AIDS. She became the head of the company.
   A scientist who invented a new drug to treat AIDS became the head of the company.

2 The company fired its Sales Director. It was taken to court.
   ....

3 The management consultants advised me. They were not very good.
   ....

4 Our computer system cost over £1m. It breaks down frequently.
   ....

5 Sven Andersson joined as Chief Executive last year. He has impressed everybody.
   ....
   ....

6 The team leader comes from Brazil. She speaks several languages.
   ....

7 Our head office is located in Zurich. It is very costly to run.
   ....

8 Our Managing Director was recruited from outside the firm. He has been very successful.
   ....
   ....

B Read the following passage about a leader. Add relative pronouns where necessary.

My favourite boss was a woman ^who^ was younger than me. She had not had a formal university education. She went straight from school to a travel firm in Cardiff, is the capital of Wales.

The firm, organised business travel and holidays for top executives, was one of the biggest travel firms in the UK. One of the top executives, met her when she was organising his firm's company trip, was really impressed with her. He hired her as his PA, meant she was able to accompany him all round the world. When he retired she succeeded him as Chief Executive and the company went from strength to strength.

She was a leader was fair but firm and was willing to deal with difficult issues immediately. Her employees, all spoke very highly of her, were very motivated. She had a clear strategy for the business her staff understood and fully supported. She was also compassionate and her secretary, had worked with her for many years, greatly admired her. She was married and had two children. Her husband, worked with her in the business, described her as a superwoman. 'She has enormous energy enables her to work harder than other people,' he said. 'She hasn't missed a single day through illness.'

Writing
Curricula vitae (resumes) and covering letters

A In the box are headings from a typical CV. Look at the extracts from the CV of Tomoko Horiguchi, a Japanese woman working in England. Under which of the CV headings should each extract be placed?

> Personal details   Education   Qualifications   Work experience
> Special skills   Interests and achievements   Referees

1 Fluent in Japanese and English   *Special skills* ....

2 Born 14 October, 1970   ....

3 Married, no children   ....

4 MBA degree from London Business School, 2001
   ....

5 Full range of computer skills
   ....

6 Aerobics, basketball, films and theatre
   ....

7 Organised a music concert while at university
   ....

8 1986–1989: Sapporo High School, Japan
   ....

9 1990–1992: Sogo Design College – studied graphic design
   ....

10 Aug–Sept 1991: Work placement at IMP (graphic design firm) Seattle, USA.
   ....

11 1993–1996: ICB (construction company) Assistant in Design Department.
   ....

12 64 Rose Park Crescent, London SW21 8CT
   ....

13 Clean driving licence   ....

14 Certificate of Proficiency in English (1995)
   ....

15 Diploma in Computing (1996)
   ....

16 Mr F. Luneau, Marketing Consultant, IMP, 120 Davis Avenue, Seattle, USA
   ....

B When you apply for a job you usually send a CV and covering letter. Which of the following do you usually do in a covering letter?

1 Say that you wish to apply and indicate where you heard about the position.

2 Say why you are interested in the job and direct the reader to special qualities, skills or experience you have.

3 Give information about your hobbies and sporting interests.

4 Provide details of your examination results.

5 Enclose the names and addresses of two referees.

6 Mention when you are available for interview.

7 Ask if there are any other vacant positions in the company.

C Study the Useful language box on the next page. Use a dictionary to check the meaning of any words or phrases which are unfamiliar. Add three words or phrases to each column.

Useful language

A Personal qualities	B Skills / activities	C Useful phrases
creative dynamic efficient energetic methodical perceptive responsible well-organised	communication skills interpersonal skills organisational ability I was responsible for … co-ordinating … developing … implementing … initiating … liaising … monitoring … negotiating … organising … reviewing … setting up	I can work / perform well under pressure. I am willing to take the initiative. I have a proven track record in … I have extensive knowledge of … I have extensive experience in / of … I am able to delegate … I can work effectively in a team. I am fluent in … I have a good knowledge of …

D Complete the letter using suitable words and phrases from the Useful language box. The letter in brackets indicates which column you should check to find the correct word or phrase.

Dear Ms Walker

I am writing to apply for the position of Managing Director which you advertised in the International Herald Tribune, dated 22 April.

I am currently employed as Marketing Director in a medium-sized cosmetics company. However I am seeking a position which will offer a greater challenge and more responsibility.

In my last job, I was responsible for _developing_ [1] (B) a sales strategy for the firm and for .... [2] (B) the work of the advertising, sales and marketing personnel. I was also involved in .... [3] (B) contracts with overseas agents and distributors, setting their sales targets and .... [4] (B) their performance. In the last six months, I have been engaged in .... [5] (B) franchising networks in Eastern Europe.

I have .... [6] (C) in the cosmetics industry, having worked for three companies dealing in health and beauty products. I think that I work well .... [7] (C) as I have organised several product launches when I had to meet tight deadlines. Although I never avoid responsibility, I am able to .... [8] (C) authority when necessary.

As for my personal qualities, I am a .... [9] (A) person, with many ideas for exciting new products which would interest your company. Most people say that I am very .... [10] (A), with the ability to motivate staff and get results. I consider myself to be extremely .... [11] (A) because I always make the most of the resources available to me.

Since you are an international company, it may interest you to know that I am .... [12] (C) in English and Spanish, and I have a working knowledge of Portuguese.

I would welcome the opportunity to meet you to discuss my application at greater length.

Yours sincerely

Gabrielle Gerard

(Ms) Gabrielle Gerard

15 Competition

Vocabulary

A **Make word partnerships with the words below. Then use them to complete the text.**

competitive	benefits
lower	leader
market	advantage
rival	costs
unique	firms

Michael Porter, a famous writer on competition, states that
competitive advantage ¹ comes from the value a firm is able to create for its
customers. This value could be based on ....² or on
............................³, which make it different from
............................⁴. The most successful firm in a sector is known as
the ....⁵, the second is the market challenger and the
remainder are market followers.

B **Rearrange each group of letters to give words commonly linked with the word** *competition.*

1	ctuoathrt	_c u t - t h r o a t_
2	kene	_ ee _
3	sogtrn	_ _ _ _ ng
4	tguoh	_ _ ug _
5	fecrei	_ ie _ _ _
6	ufiarn	_ _ _ ai _
7	isnetne	in _ _ _ _ _
8	fere	_ re _

C **Match the following words and phrases to the definitions.**

1	cartel	**a)**	to have a slight advantage over your competitor(s)
2	deregulation	**b)**	a market with only one supplier and therefore no competition
3	monopoly	**c)**	to charge a lower price than your competitor(s)
4	price fixing	**d)**	removing government rules and controls from an industry to increase competition
5	to be ahead of	**e)**	to gain complete control of a market
6	to corner the market	**f)**	to be in a better position than your rival(s)
7	to have an edge over	**g)**	a group of manufacturers who combine to stop competition and increase profits
8	undercutting	**h)**	unfair arrangement to keep prices high

D **Find a word or phrase in exercise C which refers to encouraging competition. Then find four words or phrases which refer to reducing competition.**

Language review
Talking about the future

A Complete the conversation between Pietr and Dorota about their holiday plans, using the correct form of the verb in brackets. There is often more than one correct answer.

Pietr   Where .are.............. you and your husband .going.............¹ (go) for your holidays, Dorota?

Dorota   Spain.

Pietr   That ....² (be) nice.

Dorota   Yes. We ....³ (go) to Javea for two weeks. It's near Alicante.

Pietr   When .... you ....⁴ (fly)?

Dorota   On Thursday night. Our plane ....⁵ (leave) at 9 pm from Gatwick and we ....⁶ (arrive) just before midnight in Alicante. We ....⁷ (hire) a car at Alicante and ....⁸ (drive) to Javea.

Pietr   It ....⁹ (be) great to have a break.

Dorota   Yes, but I ....¹⁰ (keep) in touch with the office by e-mail and fax.

B Choose the correct option to complete each of the following conversations.

1 A: (I'm seeing / I'll see) the Chief Executive on Tuesday. It was arranged last week.
  B: I wonder if (he'll recognise / he is recognising) you. You haven't seen him for over a year.

2 A: Look at the clouds. (It's going to / It will) rain.
  B: That's a shame. (We're not selling / We won't sell) many soft drinks this afternoon.

3 A: Do you know what time the meeting finishes?
  B: Why? What (do you do / are you doing) afterwards?

4 A: Prices (will go up / are going up) if the exchange rate changes.
  B: What (are you doing / are you going to do) if that happens?

5 A: I've just checked your flight details. Your plane for Hong Kong leaves at 9 pm.
  B: Can you find out what time the airport bus (leaves / will leaving)?

Writing
Making bookings and confirming plans

A Read the telephone message. Then read Frank Thompson's reply confirming the date of the meeting. Fill in the gaps with the correct form of words from the box.

TELEPHONE MESSAGE

To	Frank Thompson
Taken by	Sandra Johnson
From	Yuri Petrov
Company	Moscow Electronics, Russia
Telephone	+7 095 772 6391

Date 28 May

E-mail Yuri.Petrov@mosel.com

Message

Yuri Petrov wants a meeting some time between the 4th and 6th.
Please e-mail him, confirming and giving your preferred date.

---

attend	call	~~confirm~~	discuss	do	get through
		prefer	suggest		

From: Frank Thompson <Thompson@candw.com>
To: Yuri Petrov <Yuri.Petrov@mosel.com>
Date: 28 May
Re: Proposed meeting

Dear Yuri

This is to ..confirm..¹ that I'll be in Moscow from the 3rd to the 7th of August and would ....² our meeting to be on 5 August at 10 am, as we ....³.

Could you ....⁴ me a favour? Would you please ....⁵ our local distributor, Tom Harris, and ....⁶ that he ....⁷ the meeting? I've been having difficulties ....⁸ to him. I've been trying to telephone him all morning, without success. Sorry to ask you to do this, but communications between Manchester and Moscow have been terrible lately.

Best wishes

Frank

B It is two days later. Yuri Petrov e-mails Frank Thompson because he has to change the date of the meeting. Yuri knows that this will be inconvenient for Frank so he uses diplomatic language. Read the e-mail and underline all the polite phrases that Yuri uses.

From: Yuri Petrov <Yuri.Petrov@mosel.com>
To: Frank Thompson <Thompson@candw.com>
Date: 30 May
Re: Proposed meeting

Dear Frank

Something's come up, I'm afraid. I can't make it on the 5th as we arranged. I'm really sorry but I have to go to our factory at St Petersburg. We had a fire there last night which put two of our machines out of action. Sorry for the short notice, but could I suggest we meet on the 7th, in the afternoon? Would 2 pm suit you? If I don't hear from you, I'll expect to see you on the 7th.

One other thing. Don't bother to phone Tom Harris. I'll do that for you, it's the least I can do. I'm sure he'll be able to attend on the Friday. Once again, my apologies for changing the date.

All the best

Yuri

C Study the phrases in the Useful language box, then do the following tasks.

1 You are a buyer for a chain of department stores. A supplier in Poland, Katya Banaszak, has suggested that you meet in Krakow between 5 and 10 September. Write an e-mail confirming the arrangement and indicating your preferred date and time.

2 It is a week later. You find that you cannot meet Katya Banaszak on the agreed date because you have to meet an Italian supplier in Milan at the same time. Your secretary made the appointment but forgot to tell you. E-mail Katya and suggest an alternative time and date for your meeting with her. Be very diplomatic because Katya gets upset if an appointment is changed. Remember also that she is a very important supplier.

Useful language

Suggesting arrangements
Could we meet on Wednesday 4 May?
                    at 11 o'clock?
Would Thursday at 10 suit you?
Is 2:30 convenient for you? (*formal*)
How about Monday 10th? (*informal*)

Changing arrangements
I'm afraid something's come up.
Unfortunately I won't be able to make our meeting.
I'm sorry but there's a problem here at the office.

Confirming arrangements
This is to confirm that we'll be meeting on Tuesday as we agreed.
I'd like to confirm the schedule for my April trip as we arranged.

Vocabulary   Use the clues to complete the crossword puzzle.

Across

3 and **1** down. More orders for the same product. (6, 8)
5 One of the problems with .... production is that quality control is more difficult. (4)
6 *see 17 across.*
8 High quality leads to customer .... (12)
12 High quality workmanship gives a product added .... (8)
13 If something is below a certain quality level it is sub- .... (8)
16 According to the quality guru Deeming, quality is the elimination of .... (9)
17 and **6** across. No faults in a product. (4, 7)
18 *see 14 down.*

Down

1 *see 3 across.*
2 One aspect of quality control is identifying and .... mistakes during the manufacturing process. (10)
4 Quality is one area where it is important to meet customer .... (12)
7 In terms of quality, customers are always looking for value for .... (5)
9 Abbreviation of Total Quality Management. (3)
10 A special characteristic of a product or service. (7)
11 One indication of good quality is the length of the .... a manufacturer is prepared to give the customer, covering things like parts and labour. (9)
14 and **18** across. A product which has received a prize may be said to be an .... - .... product. (5, 7)
15 One indication of quality may be if the company is well-.................. (5)

Language review
Prepositions of time

Complete the report using prepositions from the box.

| at | by | during | for | in | ~~of~~ | on |

To: Head of Marketing
From: Head of R & D
Subject: Report on toy fire engine (Model PX10)
Date: 25 July

Introduction
In your memo _of_..................... [1] 1 July you asked me to prepare a short report on our new toy fire engine (Model PX10), which was withdrawn from the market .... [2] 11 June following numerous complaints by customers. The report was to be submitted .... [3] 1 August.

Findings
A number of tests have been carried out on the product .... [4] the last two weeks. The results are as follows:
- If the fire engine is operated continuously .... [5] more than two minutes, the motor breaks down.
- The wheels come off too easily, which is a safety hazard.

Recommendations
- The fire engine needs to have a more robust motor.
- The wheels need to be attached more firmly to the fire engine.
- The fire engine should not be reintroduced......................... [6] October as you requested. We recommend that it should be relaunched .... [7] the beginning of December.

Writing
Asking for payment

A There are usually three steps involved when you make written requests for payment. Study the steps in the Useful language box.

Useful language

First request
This is usually a polite enquiry. The tone of the letter or fax is neutral. You are simply reminding your customer that the account is overdue.

> We note that your account, which was due for payment on 1 July, is still outstanding.
> Could you please let us know why the balance has not been paid.
> We hope to receive your cheque by return.

Second request
This is a stronger letter or fax and its tone is firmer. However the tone should still be polite. The letter should:
- refer to the previous request and include copies of the relevant invoices.
- ask for an explanation as to why the account has not been paid.
- ask for payment to be sent.

Language work

Could you let us know why you have not settled your account?
We hope to receive a cheque from you within the next few days.
We must ask you to clear your account within 14 days.

Third request

If payment still has not been made and no explanation given, a third letter or fax must be sent. This should:

- summarise the situation and refer to previous letters or faxes.
- allow the customer a final opportunity to pay.
- inform the customer of the consequences of not paying, for example the possibility of legal action.

We note that you have not replied to our two previous requests for payment.
We must ask you to pay within 7 days.
If we do not receive payment by this time, we will have no alternative but to take legal action.

B **This fax was sent to chase payment of an unpaid invoice. Complete the fax using the words in the box.**

cheque	~~invoice~~	latest	outstanding	settle

Williams & Evans

194 Sharp Street   West Didsbury   Manchester   M20 6TW
Tel: 0161 434 2748   Fax: 0161 434 6386

FAX

If you do not receive all of the pages please telephone us immediately

To   Tina Davis, Chief Accountant, Warners Ltd
From   Teresa Lopez, Accounts Department
Date   10 March
Account No   PD 2050   *Number of pages, including this one:* 1

Dear Ms Davis

Our invoice 5280 dated 2 February

With reference to our _invoice_ .... [1] no. 5280 of 2 February, we still have not received your payment. Would you please let us have your .... [2] as soon as possible or an explanation of why the invoice is still .... [3]. We were expecting you to .... [4] your account by 28 February at the very .... [5].

I look forward to hearing from you soon.

Yours sincerely

Teresa Lopez

Teresa Lopez

C Here is the second request for the payment referred to above. Choose the correct words or phrases from the brackets to complete the fax.

To   Tina Davis, Chief Accountant, Warners Ltd
From   Teresa Lopez, Accounts Department
Date   25 March
Account No PD 2050   *Number of pages, including this one:* 3

Dear Ms Davis

I wrote to you on 10 March concerning our February [1](*bill* / *statement*). Your account is still £3,500 [2](*owing* / *overdue*). I enclose a copy of the statement and our fax.

I have not received either a reply or any [3](*payment* / *sum*) from you. I'm sure you [4](*know* / *understand*) that late payments create problems for us. I would [5](*appreciate it* / *be happy*) if you would let me know why your account has not been [6](*cleared* / *sorted*).

I must ask you to [7](*handle* / *settle*) the account [8](*by* / *within*) the next two weeks or give me reasons for not doing so. I hope you will give this [9](*business* / *matter*) your [10](*immediate* / *special*) attention.

Yours sincerely

Teresa Lopez

Teresa Lopez

D Here is the third request for payment. The paragraphs are not in the correct order. Write the correct sequence of paragraphs in the boxes provided.

To   Tina Davis, Chief Accountant, Warners Ltd
From   Teresa Lopez, Accounts Department
Date   9 April
Account No PD 2050   *Number of pages, including this one:* 4

Dear Ms Davis

☐ You have not replied to my faxes nor have you offered any explanation for not clearing your account.

☐ I wrote to you on 10 March and 25 March concerning the above account which has an outstanding balance of £3,500. I enclose copies of the faxes and a statement of your account.

☐ Please forward your payment within the next seven days. If we do not receive payment from you, we shall have no alternative but to take legal action to recover the amount.

Yours sincerely

Teresa Lopez

Teresa Lopez

E You are the credit controller for a chinaware goods manufacturer based in the South of England. One of your customers, a department store in London, has not paid its account for June. It is now July and your company is owed £8,500. Write suitable faxes for these situations.

1 It is 12 July. You still have not received payment from the department store.

2 It is 25 July. You have received no reply to your fax of 12 July requesting payment.

3 It is 5 August. You have received no reply to your previous faxes.

Talk business

Introduction

The different sounds used in English are represented by 44 different **phonemes**. Look at the **phonemic alphabet** below. It is quite easy to learn and remember the phonemic symbols. With the help of a good dictionary such as the *Longman Dictionary of Contemporary English*, these symbols will enable you to work out the pronunciation of any English word on your own. A good dictionary will also give you a definition of any words that are unfamiliar to you.

The sounds of English

🎧 **Look, listen and repeat.**

Vowel sounds

/ɪ/	'image	/ɔː/	launch
/iː/	team	/ʊ/	full
/e/	sell	/uː/	re'duce
/æ/	cash	/ʌ/	'money
/ɑː/	chart	/ɜː/	term
/ɒ/	loss	/ə/	'modern, ca'reer

Diphthongs

/eɪ/	sale	/əʊ/	flow
/aɪ/	price	/ɪə/	dear
/ɔɪ/	oil	/eə/	share
/aʊ/	a'ccount	/ʊə/	tour

Consonants

Voiceless

/p/	pay	/f/	file
/s/	sell	/θ/	think
/t/	telephone	/l/	loss
/ʃ/	option	/r/	rise
/k/	copy	/j/	year
/tʃ/	cheap	/w/	win

Voiced

/b/	buy	/v/	venture
/z/	goods	/ð/	this
/d/	deal	/h/	head
/ʒ/	decision	/m/	media
/g/	global	/n/	net
/dʒ/	joint	/ŋ/	branding

' indicates that the syllable which follows is stressed.

Tips

- Come back to this introduction and listen to the sounds of English again before doing the pronunciation activities in each unit.
- Add your own key words for each symbol in the section above.
- Identify the sounds that you have difficulty recognising or producing and focus mainly on these.
- Remember to use the pause button on your cassette or CD player. This will give you time to speak or write when you do the exercises in the *Talk business* section.

Sounds and spelling

Look at the letters in bold in each group of words. Divide the words into two groups and explain the difference between the groups.

1 c**o**st j**o**b l**o**st m**o**st **o**ffer p**o**st
Group 1: *cost, job, lost, offer*
Group 2: *most, post*
Explanation: *The 'o' in Group 2 is pronounced as in 'flow', not as in 'loss'.*

2 **k**eycard **k**nock-on **k**now-how mar**k**et
Group 1: ....
Group 2: ....
Explanation: ....
....

3 a**g**o **g**lobal **g**rowth re**g**ional strate**g**y
Group 1: ....
Group 2: ....
Explanation: ....
....

4 adj**u**st cons**u**mer pl**u**nge sec**u**rities
Group 1: ....
Group 2: ....
Explanation: ....
....

5 **b**oom **b**orrow clim**b** de**b**t
Group 1: ....
Group 2: ....
Explanation: ....
....

6 **A**pril infl**a**tion m**a**rket p**a**rtner p**a**st r**a**te t**a**ken
Group 1: ....
Group 2: ....
Explanation: ....
....

7 ann**ou**nce disc**ou**nt gr**ou**p thr**ou**gh
Group 1: ....
Group 2: ....
Explanation: ....
....

Shadowing

This is a very effective way to make the most of the recorded material.

1 Play a short section, i.e. a few words or one line of a dialogue, then pause.

2 Without speaking, repeat internally what you heard.

3 Play the same section again. Pause and speak the words in exactly the same way and at the same speed. Repeat this step until you are completely satisfied with your performance.

4 Play the same section again and speak along with the voice on the tape. This is shadowing.

5 Move on to the next short section of the tape and repeat the above procedure.

(adapted from: *The Pronunciation Book*, T. Bowen and J. Marks, Longman Group UK Limited 1992)

Introduction

UNIT 1 — Globalisation

Individual sounds

A 🎧 1.1 **Listen and underline the letters which are pronounced /ə/.**

1 It's lighter and smaller.
2 It's much bigger than Hong Kong.
3 The US dollar is much stronger than many other currencies.
4 The Moscow underground is cheaper than the one in London.

What's the rule?

–*er* is always pronounced /ə/; *than* is always pronounced /ðən/.

🎧 1.1 **Now listen again. Repeat each sentence after you hear it.**

B 🎧 1.2 **The** –*est* **ending is pronounced /ɪst/. Listen to these sentences and repeat each one after you hear it.**

1 Prices in Moscow are among the highest in Europe.
2 Cleveland is one of the cleanest cities in North America.

Connected speech

A 🎧 1.3 **Listen to the way the speaker pronounces the word** *as*. **Notice also how some of the words are linked together.**

1 Their prices are as low as ours.
2 Ireland isn't as large as Sweden.

What's the rule?

In connected speech *as* is pronounced /əz/.

B **Show where similar links could be made in these sentences.**

1 They'll have to deal with the problem as soon as possible.
2 The new photocopier is as unreliable as the old one.

🎧 1.4 **Now listen and repeat each sentence after you hear it.**

> **Tip**
>
> When you say comparative forms, such as *cheaper than* or *as large as*, stress the adjective, never *than* or *as*.

Stress and intonation

🎧 1.5 **Listen to these sentences. Underline the part of the** *phrasal verb* **(in italics) that is stressed.**

1 Nine o'clock already! I have to *ring up* the Sales Manager.
2 I didn't manage to *get through to* him.
3 I've forgotten his number. Could you *look* it *up* in the phone book for me, please?
4 He was asking about the sales report, but then we were *cut off*.
5 I'll try to *call back* later.

What's the rule?

The adverb is always stressed when:
• it is not immediately next to the verb (*see sentence 3*).
• it is at the end of the sentence (*see sentence 4*).
If the verb is in three parts, the stress is on the second part (*see sentence 2*).

Sound work

Telephoning

A 🎧 **1.6 Listen to these telephone conversations and complete the details below.**

1 First name: Tom
  Surname: ....
2 Phone (home): ....
3 Fax number: ....
4 Name: Mr Andrews
  Address: 22, ... Drive, Preston
  Post code: ....
5 Surname: ....
  Address: 15 rue ...., Brussels

🎧 **1.6 Now practise the dialogues.**

B **Complete the telephone conversations with a suitable preposition from the box.**

at	back	back	by	for	in	to	to

1 A: Could I speak .... Mark Andrews, please?
  B: I'm afraid Mr Andrews is .... a meeting at the moment.
2 A: Could I leave a message .... Frank Dawson?
  B: Yes, of course. What would you like to tell him?
3 A: Could you tell him I'll call .... tomorrow?
  B: Yes, I'll tell him as soon as he gets ....
4 A: Could you get back .... me as soon as you have the information?
  B: Yes, we'll let you know .... tomorrow afternoon .... the latest.

Socialising 1

A 🎧 **1.7 We often express agreement by saying the same thing in a different way instead of simply saying *yes*. Listen to these conversations.**

1 A: Lovely day, isn't it?
  B: Yes, beautiful.
  (low falls, B agrees)
2 A: Lovely day, isn't it?
  B: Yes, beautiful.
  (high falls, B agrees strongly)

B 🎧 **1.8 Listen to these conversations and mark the intonation used. Does B simply agree, or does he agree strongly?**

1 A: Beautiful day, isn't it?
  B: Yes, wonderful. ....
2 A: Busy morning, isn't it?
  B: Yes, hectic. ....
3 A: Interesting, this article on globalisation, isn't it?
  B: Yes, fascinating. ....

🎧 **1.8 Now practise the dialogues.**

UNIT 2   Brands

Individual sounds

A 🎧 2.1 **The –ed ending of regular verbs has three different pronunciations. Listen to the examples.**

/d/	/t/	/ɪd/
join**ed**	launch**ed**	visit**ed**

B 🎧 2.2 **Now listen to some more examples and put them in the correct column.**

/d/	/t/	/ɪd/

What's the rule?

- If the infinitive ends with /t/ or /d/, –ed is pronounced /ɪd/.
- If the infinitive ends with a voiced consonant, –ed is pronounced /d/.
- If the infinitive ends with a voiceless consonant, –ed is pronounced /t/.

Connected speech

A 🎧 2.3 **Listen to the way certain words are linked in these sentences.**

1 She worked in the sales department for eight years.
2 She became Head of Sales last August.
3 Our share price has increased sharply because of our excellent results.

What's the rule?

In each linked pair the first word finishes with a *consonant* sound and the second word begins with a *vowel* sound.

🎧 2.3 **Now listen again and repeat each sentence after you hear it.**

Stress and intonation

🎧 2.4 **Listen to the words in the following table. Underline the stressed syllable, i.e., the syllable which is spoken with more strength.**

Noun (thing)	Noun (person)	Verb
com.pe.ti.tion	com.pe.ti.tor	com.pete
dis.tri.bu.tion	dis.tri.bu.tor	dis.tri.bute
pro.mo.tion	pro.mo.ter	pro.mote
re.search	re.search.er	re.search
con.sump.tion	con.su.mer	con.sume
ad.ver.tise.ment	ad.ver.ti.ser	ad.ver.tise

🎧 2.4 **Now listen again and repeat each word after you hear it.**

Tip

One sound often appears in unstressed syllables: /ə/. It is the most common sound in English, so much so that it has a name of its own. It is called *schwa*. Noticing and practising /ə/ can help you improve your pronunciation. Highlight the /ə/ sound not only in new words but also in words you are familiar with.

First-time meetings

A **Match the phrases on the left with the appropriate reply on the right.**

1 Do keep in touch.
2 Have you been here before?
3 Nice to have met you.
4 Pleased to meet you.

a) Glad to meet you, too.
b) No, this is my first visit.
c) I'm glad to have met you, too.
d) Yes and I hope we meet again.

B **2.5 Complete the dialogue with the words you hear.**

Fiona: David, have you ....[1] our new Marketing Manager, Frances Atkinson? Frances, this is David Olsen, from CBK Ljubljana.

David: How do you do?

Frances: Pleased to meet you. How ....[2] your trip?

David: Fine, thanks. I ....[3] Swissair this time. And the weather was great.

Frances: Yes, we're lucky. It's..................[4] like this for almost a week now. Which hotel are you staying at?

David: The Calypso, as usual. Friendly service, amazing facilities and just a ten-minute walk away.

Frances: Oh, I didn't ....[5] you'd been here before.

David: Yes, three times, actually. I used to ....[6] as a consultant for your HR department.

Frances: How interesting! I suppose that was before April 1997, then. That's when I joined the company.

David: Yes, that was back in 1992–93. HR was being completely restructured. It was all very exciting.

Frances: Hmm …, you must ....[7] me more about it over lunch.

David: Yes. It's been nice talking to you. ....[8] you later.

Frances: Bye for now.

2.5 Now practise the dialogue.

Informal conversation

A **Put these sentences in the correct order to complete the conversation.**

1 Dilek: Very well thanks, Greg. And how are you?
2 Dilek: See you!
3 Dilek: I'm in a bit of a rush, I'm afraid. Give us a ring tomorrow. All right?
4 Dilek: It's been rather hectic at work, actually. Six new contracts in ten days.
5 Greg: Fine thanks. Haven't seen you for a while. What have you been up to?
6 Greg: Wow, well done!
7 Greg: Yeah. I'll be in touch. Cheers!
8 Greg: Hello, Dilek. How are things going?

2.6 Listen to check your answers. Then practise the conversation.

B **Give a more formal equivalent for each of these phrases.**

1 Hello. ....
2 What have you been up to? ....
3 I'm in a bit of a rush, I'm afraid. ....
4 Give us a ring tomorrow. ....
5 Cheers! ....

UNIT 3 Travel

Individual sounds

🎧 **3.1 Circle the sentence that you hear.**

1 **a)** They'll do it for you.   **b)** They do it for you.
2 **a)** We'll travel by air.   **b)** We travel by air.
3 **a)** I'll go to visit them on Tuesday.   **b)** I go to visit them on Tuesday.
4 **a)** You'll tell them everything.   **b)** You tell them everything.
5 **a)** They'll buy as much as possible.   **b)** They buy as much as possible.
6 **a)** We'll make all the reservations.   **b)** We make all the reservations.

What's the rule?

Notice the pronunciation of the contracted forms such as *they'll*, *we'll*, etc. The /l/ in the contractions above is called **dark l**. It is different from the **clear l** in *list*, *value*, *we'll order* for example. /l/ is clear before a *vowel* sound or /j/ but dark elsewhere, for example, *silk*, *well*, etc.

🎧 **3.1 Now listen again and practise the sentences.**

Connected speech

A In spoken English, certain sounds sometimes 'disappear'. Knowing why and where can help you understand fast speech better.

🎧 **3.2 Listen to the examples and notice how certain sounds disappear.**

1 You can't give everybody the exact seat they want.
2 Most passengers were homeward-bound commuters.

What's the rule?

/t/ and /d/ often disappear when they are between two other consonants.

B Cross out the letters that will disappear in these sentences.

1 I'll be in London next week.
2 It'll cost around five hundred pounds.
3 Can I take this as hand luggage?
4 I thought it was exempt from tax.
5 I'd like a round trip to Boston.

🎧 **3.3 Listen and check your answers.**

Stress and intonation

A 🎧 **3.4 In *wh*– questions the voice usually goes down and the main sentence stress is often on the last word. Listen to these examples.**

1 What time do I have to check in?
2 Who will pick her up at the airport?

B Underline the main stress in these sentences.

1 How much is an open ticket?
2 How long does it take to get to the station?
3 When did you confirm the arrangements?
4 Where will she be going next week?

🎧 **3.5 Listen and check your answers. Then practise the questions.**

Sound work

Asking for agreement or confirmation

A 🎧 **3.6 Listen to the intonation in these question tags.**

1 Surely there's an earlier flight, *isn't there*?

2 They've booked me into the Astoria again, *haven't they*?

What's the rule?

People frequently use question tags in spoken English to invite a response from the other person. Question tags imply a different meaning depending on the intonation used.

- If the voice rises, as in question 1, it means 'I think I'm right but I expect you to correct me if I'm not.' It is more like a real question.
- If the voice falls, as in question 2, it means 'I'm sure I'm right, and I'd like you to tell me I'm right.'

B 🎧 **3.7 Listen to these question tags and tick the correct box (↗) or (↘).**

	↗	↘
1		
2		
3		

	↗	↘
4		
5		
6		

🎧 **3.7 Now listen again and practise the sentences.**

Useful phrases

A Complete the phrases 1–6 with a suitable preposition from the box, then match them with their meaning (a–f).

in	in	in	on	over	through

1 to be .... the same wavelength

2 to be .... the moon

3 to be .... the same boat

4 to be .... the balance

5 to hear something .... the grapevine

6 .... a nutshell

a) in brief

b) soon to be decided one way or another

c) very happy

d) to think in the same way

e) to be in the same situation

f) to learn something in casual conversation with other people

B Now complete the following using the expressions above.

1 I heard .... that they're not going to pursue the merger offer.

2 Both of us agree that their offer is not acceptable. For once, we seem to be ....

3 Interest rate worries are affecting all of us. We're all ...., really.

4 Nobody knows what to expect. The future of CBK is really ....

5 I can't give you all the details now but, ..., the Luxembourg plant seems to be in serious trouble.

6 The ad campaign was a huge success and our Marketing Manager is ....

UNIT 4 Advertising

Individual sounds

A 🎧 4.1 Listen to how the speaker pronounces the /eɪ/ sound in *sales* and the /e/ sound in *sells*.

Now circle the word that you hear.

1 a) paper   b) pepper   3 a) based   b) best
2 a) saint   b) sent   4 a) date   b) debt

B 🎧 4.2 Listen to these words. Put them into the correct column according to the spelling of the /eɪ/ sound.

–a–	–ay–	–ai–	–ea–
changes			

Connected speech

🎧 4.3 How many words can you hear in each of these sentences? Contractions (such as *he'll*, *isn't*, etc.) count as two words.

1 ....   2 ....   3 ....   4 ....

Tip

To practise saying a sentence faster, start from the end, like this:
- great inconvenience
- caused us great inconvenience
- The delay's caused us great inconvenience.

🎧 4.3 Practise saying each sentence like this, then listen again. Can you repeat each sentence in the space allowed?

Stress and intonation

A 🎧 4.4 Listen to these two exchanges. Notice how Speaker B's voice goes down, or down and up.

1 A: It's a very memorable advert.   B: Yes. ↘
2 A: This will add value to our products. B: Yes. ↘↗

What's the rule?
- If you agree, your voice starts high and falls.
- If you disagree or are uncertain, your voice falls, but then rises a little.

B 🎧 4.5 Now listen and indicate whether Speaker B really agrees (↘) or not (↘↗).

1 A: What we need is a product which is really different from our competitors'.   B: Yes.
2 A: We've always used the best advertising methods.   B: Yes.
3 A: This will persuade people to choose our products.   B: Yes.

🎧 4.5 Now practise the exchanges.

Dealing with complaints

⌒ 4.6 Although serious complaints are mostly dealt with in writing, minor complaints frequently have to be dealt with face-to-face or over the phone. Listen how this can be done.

1 A: I'm ringing to let you know we still haven't received the details of your advertisement.

   B: I'm sorry to hear they haven't reached you yet. I'll look into the matter straightaway.

2 A: Jonathan Webb here. I checked our ad in the latest issue of *Ambition* magazine. I'm afraid your department has made quite a few serious errors.

   B: I'm very sorry to hear some mistakes have been made, Mr Webb. If you would give me some details I'll take the matter up at once.

3 A: Jonathan Webb speaking. Why was I not informed about the change in positioning? This is the second time this has happened.

   B: I'm terribly sorry to hear you weren't notified. I'll ask Hannah Levy to attend to it immediately.

Notice how the speaker apologises, then promises to take action.
I'm (very / terribly) sorry to hear …
I'll look into it at once.
I'll attend to it as soon as possible.
I'll take up the matter immediately.

⌒ 4.6 Now practise the dialogues.

Starting presentations

Here are the introductory sentences of two different presentations. Sort them out, then put them in a logical order.

a) Finally, I'll summarise the main reasons for the Board of Directors' confidence in Deltelcom and highlight the factors which now make our organisation fully market driven.

b) Good morning ladies and gentlemen. The theme of my presentation is the increased dividend payment that we will propose to the annual shareholders' meeting next month.

c) I'll start off by outlining the unique features of our product, after which I'll report on the results of the market research we carried out in Central and Eastern Europe.

d) I'll begin by giving you an overview of the major strategic moves which have characterised the past six months.

e) Last but not least, I shall also bring you up-to-date on the latest developments in our animatronic toy department.

f) Then, I'll fill you in on the background to the recent changes in our marketing policy.

g) Then, I'll go on to talk you through a detailed breakdown of last year's results.

h) This afternoon, I'm going to talk to you about Mamba, our new wondertoy due to be launched in November.

Mamba	Deltelcom
1	1
2	2
3	3
4	4

⌒ 4.7 Now listen and check your answers.

UNIT 5   Employment

Individual sounds

A 🎧 5.1 **Listen to the difference between /ɒ/ and /əʊ/.**

/ɒ/	/əʊ/
cost	coast
want	won't

B 🎧 5.2 **Put the words you hear into the appropriate column.**

	/ɒ/	/əʊ/
1		
2		
3		

	/ɒ/	/əʊ/
4		
5		
6		

🎧 5.2 **Now listen again and repeat each word after you hear it.**

Connected speech

🎧 5.3 **Listen to these sentences and look at the simplifications which occur.**

1 The *main p*art of the interview is the CV.
   /meɪm/

2 He wore a *light b*lue shirt at work.
   /laɪp/

3 It's all down to *good p*reparation.
   /gʊp/

4 It happened *in P*oland and *in B*ritain.
   /ɪm/   /ɪm/

5 Let's *get b*ack to the point.
   /gep/

6 It cost him *ten p*ounds fifty.
   /tem/

🎧 5.3 **Listen again and practise the sentences.**

> **Tip**
>
> In faster speech, many sounds are simplified. For instance, /d/, /n/ and /t/ at the end of a word become more like the consonant that follows. Even if you do not want to simplify your speech, being aware of sound simplifications will help improve your listening skills.

Stress and intonation

Three-syllable words can have the following stress patterns: Ooo, oOo or ooO. Put the words in the box in the correct column.

| appearance   applicant   benefits   candidate   company   dismissal |
| interview   personnel   promotion   retirement |

Ooo	oOo	ooO

🎧 5.4 **Now listen and repeat each word after you hear it.**

Sound work (side tab)

Managing meetings

Look at the skills a good chair must possess.

a) Start the meeting.

b) Ask for reactions.

c) Deal with interruptions.

d) Keep to the point.

e) Speed up or slow down whenever necessary.

f) Summarise and close the meeting.

Match these skills with the phrases or sentences below.

1 If I may just finish this point ...   ..*c*..

2 As you can see, there are two main items on the agenda.   .....

3 Does anyone have any strong views on this point?   .....

4 I think we've covered everything, so let's go over the main points briefly.   .....

5 I'm afraid that issue isn't really on today's agenda.   .....

6 Maybe I should explain that in more detail.   .....

7 That was just a brief overview. Now, let me be a bit more specific.   .....

8 Can I get back to you on that later?   .....

9 I'm afraid I fail to see the connection.   .....

10 It's been a pleasure to be with you today. We'll meet again in two weeks' time.   .....

11 Any comments on this?   .....

12 Thanks for coming. Let's get down to business.   .....

Asking for repetition

A 🎧 **5.5 Listen to how Speaker B asks for the piece of information in italics to be repeated. Notice how his voice keeps rising from the beginning of the question to the end.**

1 A: Miss Reid has invited *Mr Roberts* to lead a training session for us.

   B: Sorry, I didn't get that. Who did you say she's invited?

2 A: The seminar will be held at *our head office* on 6 July.

   B: Sorry, where will the seminar be held, did you say?

3 A: She says the main topic will be *interview techniques*.

   B: I'm afraid I didn't quite catch that. What will the main topic be?

B **Ask Speaker A to repeat the information in italics in each of these statements.**

1 A: We can offer him a fee of *$200* if he participates in the seminar.

   B: ....

2 A: He complained that *the hotel had few facilities*.

   B: ....

3 A: They didn't seem interested in *building a relationship*.

   B: ....

4 A: Our visitors are due to arrive at *9.10 on Monday the 20th*.

   B: ....

5 A: I expected *Mr Roberts* to get back to me about it.

   B: ....

🎧 **5.6 Now listen to the sample answers and practise B's responses.**

UNIT 6   Trade

Individual sounds

🎧 **6.1** **Look at the letters in bold in the words below. Listen to the words and indicate whether you pronounce the letters in bold as /ʊ/ or /uː/.**

1	val**ue**	/uː/	3 future	.....	5 producer .....
2	g**oo**ds	.....	4 reputable	.....	6 distributor .....

🎧 **6.1** **Now listen again and repeat the words.**

Connected speech

Ⓐ 🎧 **6.2** **Listen to these phrases and notice how the words are joined together.**

1 we asked	3 agree a deal	5 a day or two
2 agree on	4 they agreed	6 my assistant

What's the rule?

If a word ends in /ɪ/, /iː/, /aɪ/ or /eɪ/ and the next word begins with a *vowel* sound, we often add /j/ to link them when we speak quickly. For example *we asked* becomes /wɪjˈɑːst/, *they agreed* becomes /ðeɪjəˈɡriːd/, etc.

Ⓑ **Look at these sentences and indicate where similar links could be made.**

1 I'm sure they'll agree a deal in a day or two.
2 I asked my assistant to see to it.
3 May or June would be all right, wouldn't it?

🎧 **6.3** **Now listen to the sentences and repeat them.**

Stress and intonation

Ⓐ 🎧 **6.4** **Listen to the stress pattern of these words. Circle the odd-one-out.**

1	a) offer	b) receipt	c) discount (noun)	d) import (noun)
2	a) deliver	b) distribute	c) agreement	d) quantity
3	a) quotas	b) tariffs	c) customs	d) import (verb)

> **Tip**
>
> Some words have a different stress pattern depending on whether they are functioning as verbs or nouns. For example:
> **Verbs:** im**port**, ex**port**, in**crease**, de**crease**, pro**gress**.
> **Nouns:** **im**port, **ex**port, **in**crease, **de**crease, **pro**gress.

Ⓑ 🎧 **6.5** **Listen to the intonation in this list.**

Their major exports are flowers, seeds, bulbs and cheese.

What's the rule?

In lists, the intonation rises on each item except the last, where it falls.

Ⓒ **Mark the intonation in these lists.**

1 Their main trading partners are in Germany, Greece, Slovenia and Austria.
2 In her lecture, she talked about tariffs, quotas, dumping and deregulation.
3 Please remember to mention quantity, total value, method of payment and documents required.

🎧 **6.6** **Now listen to the sentences and repeat each one after you hear it.**

Negotiating

A Complete the sentences with the correct word from the box.

costs	delivery	discount	insurance	letter
	order	shipping	terms	

1 We could offer free delivery if you placed a large ....·

2 If you agree to quicker payment ...., we'll give you a 3% discount.

3 We'll increase our order on condition that you pay shipping ....·

4 If you covered both .... and insurance, we would place further orders with you in the near future.

5 We'll consider covering .... ourselves provided that you dispatch within five days.

6 We'll continue to offer an attractive .... so long as you agree to pay by bank transfer.

7 As long as you pay us within 30 days, we can promise .... within two weeks.

8 I'm afraid that's not acceptable unless we can pay by .... of credit.

B Which of the sentences above could be spoken by a supplier and which by a buyer.

Supplier: ..!.. ....

Buyer: ....

C Conditional sentences are often used in negotiations. List all the words and phrases used in exercise A to link the concession the speaker is prepared to make to his condition for making it.

....

....

....

....

....

....

D Look at the first four sentences in exercise A and complete the following.

1 In sentences ..... and ....., the speaker seems more confident.

2 The speaker seems less confident in sentences ..... and ......

How is this expressed?

E 🎧 6.7 Listen to these sentences. In which ones does the speaker use a past verb form?

1 .No.... 2 .... 3 .... 4 .... 5 ....

🎧 6.7 Practise saying the sentences. Note there is a rising intonation on the *if* – clause and a falling one on the main clause.

If you order within three days, we'll offer a very attractive discount.

UNIT 7 Innovation

Individual sounds

A 🎧 7.1 **Listen to how /ɜː/ is pronounced in the word *work*.
Now circle the word in each line which does not contain /ɜː/.**

1 a) heard   b) commercial   c) first   d) patent
2 a) refer   b) ingenious   c) personal   d) expert
3 a) were   b) further   c) feasible   d) world
4 a) efficient b) research   c) word   d) earn

🎧 7.1 **Listen and check your answers.**

B **Put the words in exercise A into different columns according to the spelling of /ɜː/.**

–or–					
work					

Connected speech

🎧 7.2 **Listen to these sentences and notice how the words are joined together.**

1 Hello everybody!
    /w/
2 How much do you know about those new ideas?
               /w/   /w/
3 I'd like to answer that question before I go on.
    /w/   /w/
4 You'll have to emphasise two of those points.
       /w/   /w/

What's the rule?

If a word ends in /uː/, /ʊ/, /əʊ/ or /aʊ/ and the next word begins with a *vowel* sound, we often add /w/ to link them when we speak quickly.
For example: *know about* becomes /nəʊwəˈbaʊt/ etc.

🎧 7.2 **Now listen again and repeat the sentences.**

Stress and intonation

A 🎧 7.3 **Listen how Speaker B highlights the word which is most significant in the context.**

1 A: You should buy a pager, it's very useful. | B: I've <u>got</u> a pager.
2 A: How will we be able to contact you? | B: I've got a <u>pager</u>.

B **Underline the word(s) Speaker B will highlight in these conversations.**

1 A: Where's R & D? | B: R & D is on the 2nd floor.
2 A: What's on the 2nd floor? | B: R & D is on the 2nd floor.
3 A: Did they buy a mini-bus? | B: No, they hired a mini-bus.
4 A: Did they hire a car? | B: No, they hired a mini-bus.
5 A: How about faxing them? | B: I have sent them a fax.
6 A: You could send them a letter. | B: I have sent them a fax.

🎧 7.4 **Listen to check your answers. Then listen again and take B's role.**

Making presentations

A 🎧 **7.5** **To be an effective presenter you need to think and speak in meaningful units. Pausing in the wrong places makes it difficult to understand the meaning. Listen to the example.**

B **Read this presentation extract quietly to yourself, then read it aloud. Decide on suitable pauses. Read it aloud again, recording yourself if possible.**

Although there are indications that the growth of the Hungarian market may have come to a halt, I firmly believe that it can easily be counterbalanced by further increasing exports.

If you have a look at the figures on the OHT, you will see that exports accounted for 22%, and we expect our shares to rise to 27% by the end of November.

Let us look first at the main cause of this dramatic growth in exports. As you know, the production of all our chocolate bars and breakfast cereals has been moved from Estonia and Slovakia to the south-west of Hungary ...

🎧 **7.6** **Now listen to the presentation extract and notice where the speaker chose to pause. Mark the pauses in the text as you listen again. Compare this version with your own recording.**

> **Tip**
>
> How often you pause is your own decision but there are places where you cannot pause without making it difficult to understand the meaning.

Insisting tactfully

A **Which response sounds more tactful?**

   A: I don't think I'll be able to submit the report by Friday.

1 B: I'm afraid you must submit it by Friday, otherwise we'll have to postpone the meeting.

2 B: I'm afraid it really must be submitted by Friday, otherwise we'll have to postpone the meeting.

What's the rule?

In the second response the passive is used. The passive emphasises the object, rather than the doer, and therefore makes you sound less direct, more tactful.

B **Complete these responses in a tactful way.**

1 A: Does it matter if we don't notify them today?
   B: ...., otherwise they might cancel the order.

2 A: Sorry, we won't be able to repair the printer this week.
   B: ...., otherwise the handouts won't be ready for the conference.

3 A: There's no way I can meet them at the airport.
   B: ...., otherwise they'll be offended.

4 A: I don't think we can confirm our order today.
   B: ...., otherwise we'll lose the 3% discount.

5 A: Sorry, I won't be able to translate the contract this week.
   B: ...., otherwise our suppliers will never be able to meet the deadline.

🎧 **7.7** **Listen to check your answers. Then listen again and repeat B's responses.**

Survival business English

UNIT 8 Organisation

Individual sounds

A 🎧8.1 **Listen to how /ʌ/ is pronounced in the word *money*.**

Now circle the word in each line which does not contain /ʌ/.

1 **a)** company   **b)** holiday   **c)** unlimited   **d)** bankruptcy
2 **a)** business   **b)** public   **c)** redundant   **d)** encourage
3 **a)** number   **b)** consultant   **c)** does   **d)** shareholder

🎧8.1 **Listen and check your answers.**

B **Put the words in exercise A into different columns according to the spelling of /ʌ/.**

–o–			
money			

Connected speech

A 🎧8.2 **Listen to these phrases and notice how the words are joined together.**

1 their‿assets   3 in favour‿of
2 for‿example   4 her‿assisant

What's the rule?

If a word ends in *–r* or *–re* and the next word begins with a *vowel* sound, the *–r* is usually pronounced to make a link. For example: *their assets* becomes /ðeərˈæsets/, etc.

B **Indicate where similar links could be made in these sentences.**

1 They were able to relocate their offices before April.
2 In your opinion, are there any other advantages?
3 We need more information about the car industry in the Far East.
4 They were all in favour of making her assistant redundant.

🎧8.3 **Now listen and repeat the sentences.**

Stress and intonation

🎧8.4 **Listen to these compound nouns and underline the stressed word in each.**

1 credit card   6 multinational company
2 company car   7 sole trader
3 board meeting   8 end-of-year report
4 trade barriers   9 net profit
5 profit margin   10 free trade

What's the rule?

• If a compound noun consists of *noun + noun*, the stress is *often* on the first part.
• If it consists of *adjective + noun*, the stress is *often* on the second part.

🎧8.4 **Now listen again and repeat each compound noun.**

Conversation skills

A The Marketing Manager of an overseas branch is visiting her counterpart at the head office in Newcastle. Why does the conversation break down?

A: Have you been to Newcastle before?

B: Yes, several times, actually. I was here for a management training seminar four months ago.

A: What time is your return flight tomorrow?

B Put the lines of the following dialogue into a suitable sequence.

1 A good thing you didn't miss your connecting flight! Erm … Do you actually live in Ljubljana?

2 Danila, let me introduce you to Frances Atkinson, our Marketing Manager.

3 I'd be extremely interested to go through your research results with you. Do you think we could do that first thing this afternoon?

4 Hmm …, that sounds interesting. And how about your research?

5 Pleased to meet you too. Did you have a good flight?

6 Pleased to meet you. I'm Danila Kravetz from CBK Ljubljana.

7 Well, basically, my objective was to assess the markets for our new products.

8 Well, yes, I do, but for over six months now I've been doing a research project. So I've been on tour to various parts of Eastern and Central Europe.

9 Yes, thank you, apart from a slight delay at Heathrow, it was a good trip.

🎧 **8.5** Listen to check your answers then practise the conversation.

C Provide a suitable comment and/or follow-up question for these sentences.

1 They've booked me into the Astoria as usual.

....

2 I wish I could stay longer, but I have to leave at 10.30 am tomorrow.

....

3 I'm not sure whether I should order a taxi to get to the airport.

....

> **Tip**
>
> When you give new information in answer to a question, you use a falling tone. However, too many falling tones can make you sound aggressive. To soften the effect, add a word or phrase such as *actually*, *as a matter of fact*, *I'm afraid*, *to be honest*, *to tell you the truth* or *I think*, spoken with a slightly rising tone.

D 🎧 **8.6** Listen to this conversation and mark the intonation in Speaker B's responses.

A: What's your name?

B: Heather Northcott.

A: Are you English?

B: I'm Irish, actually.

A: And where do you live?

B: In Reading.

A: What's Reading like?

B: It's not terribly exciting, to be honest.

🎧 **8.6** Listen again and repeat B's responses.

Survival business English

UNIT 9   Money

Individual sounds

A 🎧 **9.1 Listen to the difference between /aʊ/ and /əʊ/.**

/aʊ/	/əʊ/
now	no

B 🎧 **9.2 Put the words you hear into the correct column.**

	/aʊ/	/əʊ/
1		
2		
3		

	/aʊ/	/əʊ/
4		
5		
6		

Connected speech

🎧 **9.3 Listen to the way *was* and *were* are pronounced in these sentences.**

1 Other indices were also positive.
2 They said the fall was in line with market expectations.
3 Bangkok Bank was the most active stock.
4 Leading Internet stocks were boosted by a series of ratings changes.
5 Local investors were awaiting news of the fate of the Commerce Bank.

🎧 **9.3 Listen again and repeat the sentences. Use the weak forms, /wəz/, /wə/ and /wər/.**

> **Tip**
>
> To improve your pronunciation, use the weak forms when *was* or *were* appear within the sentence or at the beginning (see also Unit 10).

Stress and intonation

A 🎧 **9.4 Listen to the intonation in these two examples.**

1 A: Who did you meet this morning? | B: I met Olga this morning.
2 A: When did you meet Olga? | B: I met Olga this morning.

What's the rule?

We use a falling tone when we give new information. If the information is shared with the hearer, we use a fall-rise.

B **Read the following exchanges and decide whether Speaker B will use a fall (↘) or a fall-rise (↘↗).**

1 A: How do they feel about the profits? | B: They're worried about the profits.
2 A: What are they worried about? | B: They're worried about the profits.
3 A: Our next meeting is in October. I'd very much like you to chair it. | B: I'm afraid I'm going to France in October.
4 A: When you're in Paris this summer, don't miss Kate's training seminar. | B: I'm afraid I'm going to France in October.

🎧 **9.5 Now listen to the exchanges and repeat B's responses.**

Correcting information

A 🎧 **9.6 The word we stress most in a sentence is the one we consider most important. When we deal with figures we need to be accurate. Listen how stress is used to correct inaccuracies.**

The correct information is *The shares rose 60 cents to 22.30.*

1 A: The shares rose 50 cents to 22.30.
  B: That's not quite right. They rose <u>six</u>ty cents.

2 A: The shares rose 60 cents to 22.40.
  B: I'm afraid that's not correct. They rose to twenty-two point <u>thir</u>ty.

3 A: The shares rose to 24.30.
  B: That's not quite right, I'm afraid. They rose to twenty-<u>two</u> point thirty.

B **Underline what Speaker B will stress most to correct these inaccuracies.**

The correct amount is *DM 3.7 bn.*
The correct period is *the first quarter of the year.*

1 A: The bank took DM 3.7 bn in risk provisions to cover property losses in the second quarter of the year.
  B: I'm afraid that's not correct. The property losses were in the first quarter of the year.

2 A: The bank took DM 3.3 bn in risk provisions to cover property losses in the first quarter of the year.
  B: It seems you haven't got all your figures right. They took DM 3.7 bn in risk provisions.

3 A: The bank took DM 2.7 bn in risk provisions to cover property losses in the first quarter of the year.
  B: That's not quite right, I'm afraid. They took DM 3.7 bn in risk provisions.

🎧 **9.7 Now listen to the exchanges and repeat B's replies.**

Describing trends

Complete these sentences about the graph with a suitable word. Then put them in a logical sequence.

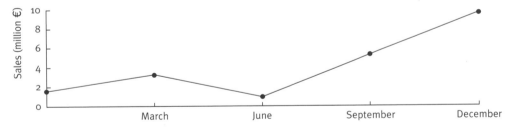

1 We'll be looking at the reasons .... this spectacular recovery in a moment.
2 First, I suggest we have a look .... this graph.
3 .... the end of July, however, we had already recovered.
4 This was followed by a drop, owing .... a poor sales promotion campaign for our new range of products as well as serious distribution difficulties.
5 We made a reasonable start at 1.7 million and, rather unexpectedly, sales went .... moderately till the end of the first quarter.
6 Sales started to take off .... the beginning of August, to reach a record high by the end of December.
7 It shows last year's sales figures, all expressed .... euros.

🎧 **9.8 Now listen to the presentation and repeat each sentence.**

UNIT 10   Ethics

Individual sounds

A 🎧10.1 **Listen to the difference between /æ/ and /ʌ/.**

/æ/	/ʌ/
began	begun

B 🎧10.2 **Put the words you hear into the correct column.**

	/æ/	/ʌ/			/æ/	/ʌ/
1				3		
2				4		

Connected speech

A 🎧10.3 **Listen to the strong and weak forms of these *auxiliary verbs*.**

	Strong form	Weak form
was	/wɒz/	/wəz/
were	/wɜː/	/wə/
had	/hæd/	/həd/
has	/hæz/	/həz/
have	/hæv/	/həv/

B 🎧10.4 **Listen to the following exchanges and indicate whether the strong or the weak form is used.**

1 A: Were they really employing people illegally?   ......*weak*......
  B: Yes, they were.   ......*strong*......
2 A: Was he using the office phone for private purposes?   ....
  B: Well, yeah, it seems that he was.   ....
3 A: Had they been prosecuted before?   ....
  B: They had, actually. Back in 1997.   ....
4 A: They've been accepting bribes.   ....
  B: Have they really?   ....

🎧10.4 **Listen again and practise the exchanges.**

> **Tip**
>
> Being familiar with these weak forms will help make your speech sound more natural. It will also improve your listening skill.

Stress and intonation

Circle the word which has a different stress pattern.

1 a) trustworthy   b) ethical   c) illegal
2 a) bribery   b) evasion   c) laundering
3 a) deceit   b) devious   c) sentence
4 a) burgle   b) commit   c) accuse
5 a) espionage   b) corruption   c) honesty

🎧10.5 **Now listen and check your answers.**

Problem solving

Match the requests for advice on the left with a suitable response on the right.

1 This is the fourth time Nick has rung in sick. What do you think we should do about it?

2 The new deputy manager is putting pressure on Elaine to go out with him. What do you suggest we do?

3 She has serious concerns about frauds with government contracts. Don't you think something should be done about it?

4 I don't really trust our new accountant. I'm sure those errors were deliberate. Any idea how we should address this issue?

5 He has hinted once again that his niece would be the best person for the job. What shall we do?

a) How about telling him it's not on? Nepotism is a thing of the past, isn't it?

b) Have you thought of confronting him with the issue? He may have genuine health problems.

c) I suggest you check his personal file first to see if he's ever been accused of sexual harassment.

d) I think we should tell her not to speak to anybody. The issue is far too serious.

e) If I were you, I'd give her another chance. Honestly, she doesn't look the type of person who'd make false entries in the accounts.

Now underline the phrases used for giving advice.

Tactful suggestions

A Choose the more tactful reply to each statement.

1 Let's give them till March.

   a) That's too late.   b) Isn't that too late?

2 I suggest we meet again in May.

   a) April would be better   b) Wouldn't April be better?

Tip

A negative question is an easy way to make a suggestion pleasantly.

B Make these suggestions more tactful.

1 We should talk to him first.

....

2 It would be better to let her know today.

....

3 We could postpone making a decision.

....

4 They are too expensive.

....

5 We had better cancel the deal.

....

6 We have to tell them the truth about the bribes.

....

7 They will be embarrassed if we mention tax evasion.

....

🎧 10.6 **Listen to check your answers.**

Survival business English

UNIT 11   Change

Individual sounds

A 🎧 **11.1 Listen to the difference between /v/ and /w/.**

/v/	/w/
of	one

B 🎧 **11.2 Put the words you hear into the correct column.**

	/v/	/w/
1		
2		
3		
4		
5		
6		

	/v/	/w/
7		
8		
9		
10		
11		
12		

C 🎧 **11.3 Listen then repeat these sentences.**

1 It's one of my favourite venues.
2 Vic was working with the new Chief Executive.
3 Vesna explained her vision to everybody.

Connected speech

🎧 **11.4 Complete the sentences with the words you hear.**

1 .... like .... begin?
2 .... really .... agree ....
there.
3 .... move .... next
.... agenda.
4 How .... that?
5 .... explain ....
.... more clearly?

🎧 **11.4 Listen again and practise the sentences.**

Stress and intonation

🎧 **11.5 Listen to this quotation from Jack Welch, CEO of General Electric, and underline the words the speaker chooses to stress most.**

We want to be a company that is constantly renewing itself, leaving the past behind, adapting to change. Managements that hang on to weakness for whatever reason – tradition, sentiment, or their own management weakness – won't be around in the future.

🎧 **11.5 Listen again then practise reading the quotation.**

Tip

Reading aloud is an easy and effective way to practise your pronunciation. Even when you work on your own you become aware of areas that require attention.

Agreeing and disagreeing 1

Match each statement on the left with a suitable response on the right.

1 Quality has a lot to do with appearance.
2 I still see that region as a very significant market.
3 Our net profits are still up.
4 I think the companies to watch are the car manufacturers.
5 So what I suggest is that we give them a 5% increase.
6 We just have to invest more in our Belgian plant.

a) I agree with you up to a point, but don't forget that their capacity is being cut drastically.
b) I'm afraid I can't agree with you there. That's a lot more than we can afford.
c) That's right. In fact, they're soaring.
d) That's out of the question, I'm afraid. It's far too inefficient. We should close it down.
e) You're absolutely right. I think we should strengthen our presence there.
f) Yes, I'm in total agreement with you there. We need to make our packaging more attractive.

🎧 11.6 **Listen to check your answers.**

Now underline the phrases used to express agreement or disagreement.

Asking for clarification

Match each interruption on the left with the appropriate accompanying question on the right.

1 Can I just ask a question at this point? You were telling us why the economy in Asia and South America remains difficult.
2 Sorry, could I stop you there for a moment? I'd like to go back to something you said earlier about your ability to deliver high profits regardless of market conditions.
3 If I may interrupt, there's something I'm not sure I fully understood. You said you expected a 10% increase in sales next year.
4 If it's all right, there's a question I'd like to ask. When you were describing the plans for the restructuring of the Luxembourg plant, you hinted that redundancies were not unlikely.
5 Sorry for cutting in on you. You said you were in favour of a limited licensing agreement.

a) Could you be a little more specific about what you mean by 'high profits' and tell us exactly how much pre-tax profit you expect?
b) Could you tell us a bit more about the consequences of those plans and if possible specify how many people might be in danger of being laid off?
c) Could you specify what you mean by 'limited' please?
d) Could you elaborate on that and explain how you think such an increase can be achieved considering that the market in the region seems to have come to a halt?
e) Could you go over what you said about the Far East again, please, and tell us what the prospects might be in the next two years?

🎧 11.7 **Listen to check your answers.**

Now underline the phrases used when interrupting and when asking for clarification.

UNIT 12   Strategy

Individual sounds

A 🎧 **12.1** **Listen to the difference between /ɔː/ and /əʊ/.**

/ɔː/	/əʊ/
hall	whole
court	coat

B 🎧 **12.2** **Put the words you hear into the correct column.**

	/ɔː/	/əʊ/
1		whole
2		
3		
4		
5		

	/ɔː/	/əʊ/
6		
7		
8		
9		
10		

Connected speech

🎧 **12.3** **Listen to the way these *prepositions* are pronounced.**

1 This product has been withdrawn *from* the market *for* eight months.
2 It might be re-launched *at* Easter.
3 You haven't contacted us *for* two weeks.
4 The meeting was due to start *at* nine.
5 Unibank is an obvious target *for* us *for* a merger.
6 We see no reason to change our position *at* this point.

Now indicate where the preposition links with the next word.

What's the rule?

When a preposition occurs in the middle of a sentence the weak form is usually used. For example: *from* becomes /frəm/, *at* becomes /ət/ and *for* becomes /fə/.

Stress and intonation

🎧 **12.4** **Listen to these word partnerships and underline the syllables which are stressed.**

1 to pe.ne.trate a mar.ket
2 to reach an ob.jec.tive
3 to de.ve.lop a stra.te.gy
4 to im.ple.ment a plan
5 to con.si.der a pro.po.sal

6 to dis.tri.bute a pro.duct
7 to ter.mi.nate a con.tract
8 to re.lo.cate a fac.tory
9 to ac.cept an of.fer
10 to a.ban.don a pro.ject

🎧 **12.4** **Listen again and practise the word partnerships.**

Tip

Record and learn words together with those that occur regularly with them.

Sound work

Sounding decisive

A **Look at these sentences. Which is the more decisive?**

1 We need a new advertising strategy.
2 What we need is a new advertising strategy.

Tip

One way of sounding decisive is to change the word order. The second sentence has more weight and catches the listener's attention.

🎧12.5 **Now listen to the intonation used.**

What we need is a new advertising strategy.

B **Rewrite these sentences to sound more decisive.**

1 They are particularly interested in a joint venture.

....

2 We intend to target the French market.

....

3 He wants to restructure the Dortmund plant.

....

4 We're not trying to change the whole procedure.

....

5 They'd like to buy up a lot of shares quickly.

....

🎧12.6 **Listen to check your answers. Then practise the sentences.**

C 🎧12.7 **Listen to these sentences. Which is the more decisive in each pair?**

1 **a)** I'd like to hear your opinion on this.　　**b)** I would like to hear your opinion on this.

2 **a)** It hasn't been a success.　　**b)** It has not been a success.

3 **a)** We want to act.　　**b)** We do want to act.

Tip

Using extra stress is another way to make a statement sound more decisive. In the second sentence in each case the *auxiliary* or the word *not* is stressed, giving more weight to what is said.

D **Rewrite these sentences to sound more decisive.**

1 It's made losses every year.

....

2 It'll make a profit in the end.

....

3 Our products don't seem to appeal to French people.

....

4 That's a problem.

....

5 We need a new strategy.

....

🎧12.8 **Listen to check your answers then practise the sentences.**

Survival business English

UNIT 13   Cultures

Individual sounds

🎧13.1   **Listen to how /iː/ is pronounced in the word *team*.**
Then put the words you hear into the correct column according to the spelling of the /iː/ sound.

–ea–	–e–	–ee
team		

Connected speech

A 🎧13.2   **When we use modal verbs to refer to past situations we often use *modal verb + auxiliary + past participle*. Listen to how the auxiliary is pronounced in these sentences.**

  1   They should have arrived at ten o'clock.
                 /əv/

  2   They shouldn't have sent such a young person to negotiate a contract in China.
                 /əf/

  3   He must have been disappointed by the food.
              /əv/

What's the rule?

- When *have* is used between a modal verb and a past participle the weak form, /əv/, is always used.
- If *have* is followed by a voiceless consonant the weak form, /əf/, is often used.

B   **Read these sentences. Indicate whether *have* is pronounced /əv/ or /əf/.**

  1   You might have tried to show more cultural sensitivity. ....
  2   If they'd known their visitors were Muslims, they wouldn't have ordered pork for dinner. ....
  3   If they'd planned their visit better, they wouldn't have begun the negotiation by announcing their deadlines. ....

🎧13.3   **Listen then repeat the sentences. Notice where the words are linked.**

Stress and intonation

A 🎧13.4   **Listen to these exchanges.**

  1   A: Did you have a good time with your Lithuanian visitors?
       B: Yes, I found them very friendly.

  2   A: Did your Japanese visitors enjoy the reception?
       B: Yes, ...but they thought it was rather noisy.

In exchange 1 Speaker B sounds sincere and enthusiastic; her voice starts high and then falls. In exchange 2 she is expressing doubt or reservation; her voice goes down a little, then rises a little.

B 🎧13.5   **Listen to these exchanges. Does Speaker B give an enthusiastic reply or express doubt or reservation?**

1	A: Looking forward to the meeting?	B: Yes.
2	A: Our new receptionist is doing well.	B: She's very efficient.
3	A: What was it like in Slovenia?	B: People were very sociable.

🎧13.5   **Now listen again and practise the exchanges.**

Sound work

Socialising 2

A 🎧 **13.6 Listen to these exchanges. Which person sounds more interested?**

1 A: The seminar was very useful. | B: Was it?
 | C: Was it?

2 A: Their new Head is extremely efficient. | B: Is she?
 | C: Is she?

B **Write an appropriate follow-up question to each of these statements.**

1 A: This is my first visit here.
 B: *Is it?* ....Yes.......

2 A: They've booked me into The Royal.
 B: ....

3 A: There are lots of interesting concerts on at the moment.
 B: ....

4 A: I'd be interested in a walk round the Old Town.
 B: ....

5 A: I'm free tomorrow evening.
 B: ....

🎧 **13.7 Now listen to the exchanges. Does Speaker B sound interested?**

🎧 **13.7 Listen again and repeat the follow-up questions.**

Adding emphasis

A **Look at these sentences. Which is the more emphatic?**

1 I hope the economy in the region will recover quickly.
2 I very much hope the economy in the region will recover quickly.

> **Tip**
>
> Using an intensifying adverb can help emphasise what you say.

B **Look at these common combinations of adverbs and verbs.**

| completely
fully
totally
entirely } agree | fiercely
firmly
vigorously
strongly } oppose | sincerely
very much } hope |
| firmly
honestly
truly
sincerely } believe | strongly
completely
totally
utterly } disagree | deeply
sincerely
very much } regret

strongly
highly } recommend |

Choose a suitable adverb from those above to make these statements sound more emphatic.

1 We recommend their new XJ3 ink-jet printer.
2 We regret the inconvenience this error has caused you.
3 We will oppose plans for a joint venture.
4 I believe we should give them more incentives.

🎧 **13.8 Listen to the sample answers and practise them.**

UNIT 14 Leadership

Individual sounds

A 🎧 14.1 **Listen to the difference between /θ/ and /ð/.**

/θ/	/ð/
think both	this smooth

B 🎧 14.2 **Put the words you hear into the correct column.**

	/θ/	/ð/			/θ/	/ð/
1	wealth			6		
2				7		
3				8		
4				9		
5				10		

🎧 14.2 **Now listen again and practise the words.**

Connected speech

A 🎧 14.3 **How many words do you hear in each sentence? Count contractions such as *you're* and *they've* as two words.**

1 ....
2 ....
3 ....
4 ....
5 ....

🎧 14.3 **Now listen again and practise the sentences.**

B **Show where links could be made in these sentences.**

1 Shall we bring forward our annual meeting to 30 November?
2 There is another seminar on Thursday, 23 of August.
3 They have postponed their visit until the 13th.
4 Why is 5 April such an important date?
5 Let's meet at 10.30 on Tuesday, 9 June.

🎧 14.4 **Now listen and repeat the sentences. Notice how the dates are spoken.**

Stress and intonation

🎧 14.5 **Listen to these words. Underline the stressed syllable in each word. Then circle the odd-one-out.**

1	**a)** de<u>ci</u>sive	**b)** agg<u>ress</u>ive	**c)** <u>sen</u>sitive
2	**a)** passionate	**b)** impulsive	**c)** flexible
3	**a)** charismatic	**b)** motivating	**c)** sympathetic
4	**a)** accessible	**b)** energetic	**c)** adventurous
5	**a)** moderate	**b)** thoughtful	**c)** sincere

Sound work

Saying what you mean

A 🎧 **14.6 Listen to these sentences and mark the pauses.**

1 The manager who trusts his staff will make a good leader.
2 The manager, who trusts his staff, will make a good leader.

What's the rule?

Pausing in different places can change the meaning of what you say. Sentence 1 means that if managers trust their staff they will make good leaders. Sentence 2 means that this particular manager trusts his staff and so will make a good leader.

B 🎧 **14.7 Listen to these sentences then match them with their meaning.**

1 The local investors who opposed the deal are now feeling sorry.

2 The local investors, who opposed the deal, are now feeling sorry.

3 We should discontinue production of the lightweight models which are no longer in big demand.

4 We should discontinue production of the lightweight models, which which are no longer in big demand.

5 He says his sister who lives in Paris is a born leader.

6 He says his sister, who lives in Paris, is a born leader.

a) Those who didn't oppose the deal are satisfied.

b) All of the local investors are feeling sorry as they all opposed the deal.

c) None of the lightweight models are in big demand.

d) Some lightweight models are no longer in demand.

e) He only has one sister.

f) He has more than one sister.

Giving explanations

A Look at how *relative pronouns* are used when explaining words in these exchanges.

1 A: What's a 'hacker'?
  B: It's someone *who* uses a computer illegally to break into computerised information systems.

2 A: What do you mean by 'going rate'?
  B: The going rate is the price for a product or service *which* the market will accept.

B Complete the following exchanges with a suitable relative pronoun.

1 A: What's a profit and loss account?
  B: It's an account .... shows a company's revenue and expenditure.

2 A: What's a head-hunter?
  B: It's someone .... tries to persuade someone to leave their job and accept a job with a different company.

3 A: What do you mean by intangible assets?
  B: They are assets .... are difficult to quantify, like trade marks or patents, for instance.

4 A: What's an ombudsman?
  B: It's someone .... works for the government or for an organisation, and deals with the complaints made against it.

🎧 **14.8 Listen to check your answers. Then listen again and repeat B's responses.**

Survival business English

UNIT 15   Competition

Individual sounds

A Circle the word in which the sound in bold is different.

1	a) sh**a**re	b) unf**ai**r	c) f**ie**rce
2	a) **lea**der	b) comp**e**te	c) h**ea**vy
3	a) t**ough**	b) alth**ough**	c) foll**ow**
4	a) aver**age**	b) advant**age**	c) un**i**que
5	a) aggress**i**ve	b) f**i**rm	c) d**i**rty
6	a) r**i**val	b) ad**a**pt	c) ch**a**llenge

🎧 15.1   Now listen to the words and repeat them.

B 🎧 15.2   Listen to these words containing the letters –ea–. Put them into four groups according to their pronunciation.

1 ....

2 ....

3 ....

4 ....

Connected speech

🎧 15.3   Complete these sentences about the future with the words you hear.

1 She .... for a new job.

2 What time .... these visitors ....?

3 I .... a new client tomorrow at ten o'clock.

4 There are clear signs that they .... bankrupt.

5 .... to watch my presentation this afternoon?

6 The plane for Rome .... at 9.30.

7 The company .... 20 years old next Wednesday.

8 They .... the day after tomorrow.

9 The agreement .... in 20 months' time.

10 The train .... at 14.45.

🎧 15.3   Now listen again and practise the sentences.

Stress and intonation

🎧 15.4   Listen to these sentences and underline the stressed words.

1 The sources of cost advantage are varied and depend on the structure of the industry.

2 The means of differentiation are peculiar to each industry.

3 Differentiation can be based on the product itself, the delivery system by which it is sold, the marketing approach and a broad range of other factors.

4 Focus rests on the choice of a narrow competitive scope within an industry.

5 A firm that engages in each strategy but fails to achieve any of them is stuck in the middle.

Tip

You can't choose which syllable to stress in a word. At the sentence level, however, you can choose which words to stress more depending on the meaning you wish to convey and the overall context.

Making an appointment

MONDAY	
am	
pm	*Brief sales reps*
TUESDAY	
am	*Show Korean visitors round factory*
pm	
WEDNESDAY	
am	
pm	*Presentation to sales conference*
THURSDAY	
am	*Visit Antwerp plant*
pm	

Look at Chris Brown's diary on the left and then complete the conversation below with suitable responses.

A: Good morning, Chris. David Olsen here. When can I see you about the trade fair.

B: Good morning, David. Let me just have a look at my diary. Erm ... When would be a convenient time for you?

A: Well, Monday afternoon would be perfect.

B: I'm afraid I'm briefing our new sales reps then, but I'm free in the morning.

A: That's no good, I'm afraid. How about Tuesday morning?

B: ....¹

A: Well, Wednesday afternoon would suit me fine.

B: ....²

A: I can't make Wednesday morning. Thursday morning, maybe?

B: ....³
But how about the afternoon? I could see you when I get back, say 2 pm?

A: Thursday at 2 pm. Great! See you then.

🎧15.5 **Listen to the sample answers then practise the dialogue.**

Agreeing and disagreeing 2

A 🎧15.6 Listen to how Speaker B stresses the auxiliary to express agreement or tactful disagreement.

1 A: We'll have to give them a discount.
   B: Yes, we certainly <u>will</u> have to give them more favourable terms.

2 A: We'll have to give them a discount.
   B: Actually I'm not sure we <u>will</u> have to give them more favourable terms.

B Write a statement agreeing with Speaker A and underline the most stressed word.

1 A: Don't you think we should alter the specifications?
   B: ....

2 A: It looks as if we'll need a different strategy.
   B: ....

3 A: It'll be quicker to fax them.
   B: ....

4 A: It seems they are expecting a reply by Thursday.
   B: ....

🎧15.7 **Now listen to the sample answers and repeat B's responses.**

C Write a statement disagreeing tactfully with Speaker A and underline the most stressed word.

1 A: The lightweight model would be too expensive.
   B: ....

2 A: Their prices will go up from March 1st.
   B: ....

3 A: The printer is now working properly.
   B: ....

4 A: The rate of exchange is going to increase again, it seems.
   B: ....

🎧15.8 **Now listen to the sample answers and repeat B's responses.**

UNIT 16 — Quality

Individual sounds

A 🎧16.1 **Many long words end in *–tion* or *–sion*. Listen to the way they are pronounced.**

ex.pec.<u>ta</u>.tion   ex.pla.<u>na</u>.tion   re.com.men.<u>da</u>.tion
dis.il.<u>lu</u>.sion   su.per.<u>vi</u>.sion   de.<u>ci</u>.sion

What's the rule?

If a word ends in *–tion* or *–sion*, the stress is always on the syllable just before the ending. Notice that *–tion* is pronounced /ʃən/ and *–sion* is pronounced /ʒən/.

B 🎧16.2 **Now listen to these words. Underline the stressed syllable.**

1 e.li.mi.na.tion   3 com.pen.sa.tion
2 va.ri.a.tion   4 pre.ci.sion

Connected speech

Look at the *Connected speech* section in the previous units. Mark in this extract where the links are, where sounds change or disappear, and where weak forms occur.

Rolls-Royce duly went bust in nineteen seventy-three. The trouble with old-style quality, it seemed, was that it encouraged supply-driven management. The engineers would make the product to the highest possible standard and price it accordingly. If the public was so uncultured that they turned it down, so much the worse for the public. And so old-style quality got a bad name in business circles. It was all very well for artists to produce masterpieces. The job of companies was to please the market.

🎧16.3 **Now underline the main sentence stresses in the extract. Then listen to one possible answer.**

Stress and intonation

Match each complaint on the right with a suitable reply on the left.

1 I was promised delivery ten days ago and the goods still haven't arrived.

2 We've just received an invoice for goods we never ordered.

3 I'm afraid I'm still waiting for that fax your Sales Manager promised to send yesterday morning.

4 The photocopier you delivered last week doesn't seem to work properly.

a) Sorry to hear that. What exactly seems to be the problem?

b) Oh dear! Sorry to hear that. Could you give me the reference number?

c) I'm very sorry there's been a delay. I'll look into the matter straightaway.

d) I'm afraid he isn't in at the moment, but I'll make sure he gets back to you as soon as possible.

🎧16.4 **Listen to check your answers. Pay attention to the intonation used in the replies. Then listen again and repeat the replies.**

Polite requests in meetings

A 🎧 **16.5 Listen to this polite request.**

Would you like to start?

B 🎧 **16.6 You will hear the same request spoken twice. One sounds polite and one sounds rude or bored. Which one sounds polite in each case, a) or b)?**

1 Could you explain what you mean by quality? ....
2 Would you mind going over that again? ....
3 Excuse me. Could you repeat your example? ....
4 Could we get back to the main point? ....
5 Could we move on to the next point? ....
6 Excuse me. Could I come in here? ....
7 Sorry, I didn't quite follow you. Could you explain that again?
 ....

C 🎧 **16.7 Listen to the requests above. They are all spoken with polite intonation. Repeat each one after you hear it.**

Dealing with problems

What are these small problems about? Choose from the box below. There may be more than one answer to each.

| computer | drinks machine | fax | lift | photocopier | telephone |

1 It's crashed again. ....
2 Oh no, it's jammed! ....
3 I can't get through. ....
4 It keeps saying 'Navigation cancelled'. ....
5 Out of paper! Just my luck. ....
6 It's still not working properly. ....
7 It's out of order. ....
8 It's completely bust. ....

Now match these offers of help with the problems above. There may be more than one answer to each.

a) Don't worry, I'll try to call them later. ....
b) There must be something wrong with the server.
   I'll go and enquire. ....
c) Let's try and remove that crumpled paper down there. ....
d) I'll order some right away. ....
e) We'll have to have it serviced again, it seems. ....
f) Let's call systems support. ....
g) I'll call the engineer. ....
h) Shall I send it to be repaired? ....

Answer key

Language work

1 Globalisation

Vocabulary

1 globalisation
2 acquisition
3 Expansion
4 controlling interest
5 joint ventures
6 domestic
7 targeted
8 overseas

1 f   2 g   3 c   4 a   5 i   6 d   7 b   8 h   9 j   10 e

Before call
look up

Starting call
get through
hold on
pick up
put through

During call
cut off
speak up

Ending call
hang up

After call
call back
get back to

1 look it up
2 Hold on
3 got through
4 put me through
5 speak up
6 get back to
7 call you back
8 cut off
9 hang up
10 pick up

Language review

Sample answers
1 The Mobile XJ2 is smaller than the Cell XL1.
2 The Mobile XJ2 has a longer guarantee than the Cell XL1.
3 The Mobile XJ2 is more expensive than the Cell XL1.

C

1 more cheap = cheaper
2 more better = better
3 dryer = drier
4 exoticer = more exotic
5 more great = greater

2 Brands

Vocabulary

1 b   2 f   3 d   4 g   5 a   6 h   7 e   8 c

1 cash cow
2 niche
3 upmarket
4 promote
5 market share
6 loss leader

C

1 new product development
2 unique selling point (proposition)
3 point of sale
4 public relations
5 research and development
6 strengths   weaknesses   opportunities   threats

D

Noun (thing)	Noun (person)	Verb
competition	competitor	compete
distribution	distributor	distribute
promotion	promoter	promote
research	researcher	research
consumption	consumer	consume
advertisement / advert / ad / advertising	advertiser	advertise

1 competition   2 competitor   3 compete

developing
domestic
down
established
expanding
mass
new
niche
overseas
shrinking
up

MARKET

forces
leader
niche
place
price
research
sector
share
survey

Niche goes both before and after.

Language review

A

1	left	7	has been
2	went	8	reorganised
3	joined	9	has increased
4	worked	10	has risen
5	became	11	have cut
6	haven't had	12	launched

B

1	visited	9	haven't received
2	gave	10	has had
3	was	11	left
4	met	12	has been
5	informed	13	have fallen
6	has complained	14	have phoned/phoned
7	went	15	have just finished
8	had		

3 Travel

Vocabulary

A

1 c 2 d 3 c 4 c 5 d
6 a 7 a 8 e 9 a 10 f
11 f 12 b 13 b 14 e 15 a
16 b 17 a 18 d 19 b 20 b

B

Verb	Noun (thing)	Noun (person)
commute	commuting	commuter
immigrate	immigration	immigrant
travel	travel	traveller
tour	tourism	tourist
visit	visit	visitor

B

Land	Sea	Air
breakdown	disembark	check-in
platform	surcharge	gate
rush hour	upgrade	runway
sleeper		surcharge
tailback		terminal
traffic-jam		turbulence
		upgrade

Language review

1 a 2 b 3 b 4 b 5 a 6 a 7 c

Writing

A

1 concerned
2 inconvenience
3 looked into
4 sincere apologies
5 Unfortunately
6 compensate
7 to offer you
8 Once again
9 the difficulties you encountered
10 to my attention
11 in the future

B

4, 5, 3, 1, 2, 6

4 Advertising

Vocabulary

A

1	Gaining	5	Giving
2	Capturing	6	Adding
3	Opening	7	Helping
4	Differentiating		

B

1 a 2 b 3 a 4 c 5 a 6 b 7 c 8 a 9 b 10 a

Language review

A

1	the	6	the	11	–
2	–	7	–	12	–
3	a	8	The	13	the
4	–	9	an	14	–
5	a	10	the	15	the

B

No article	The
Continents and most countries Africa, Asia, Brazil, China, India	Countries whose name includes unions or plurals Netherlands, Philippines, United Kingdom, United States of America
States and counties Oxfordshire, Texas	Geographical features and most geographical regions Baltic Sea, Far East, Middle East, Punjab, Sahara, Thames
Towns and cities London, New York, Vancouver	Island groups Channel Islands, West Indies
Most streets Broadway, Pennsylvania Avenue	Hotels Hilton, Holiday Inn, Ritz

'What's **the** best advert you've ever seen?'

'Well, I remember I was reading **a** newspaper in **the** Holiday Inn near Heathrow airport. I had just returned to **the** United Kingdom from a marketing trip to ~~the~~ New York. I'd been staying in the Ritz. Anyway the newspaper – I think it was **the** *Financial Times* – had an article about what was **the** best advert of the century. I think one of *Marlboro*'s cigarette adverts was voted **the** best. However I have always liked ~~the~~ *Coca Cola*'s adverts. I think it would be interesting to look at what adverts are popular in different cultures. Would an advert that was popular in the United States also be popular in ~~the~~ Africa or ~~the~~ Asia?'

Writing

1 just received
2 sorry
3 confirming
4 Unfortunately
5 occurred
6 specified
7 made it clear
8 absolutely vital
9 inconvenience
10 affect
11 feel unable to
12 consider this acceptable
13 receiving
14 as soon as possible

3, 5, 2, 1, 4

5 Employment

Vocabulary

A

1 promote
2 fire
  sack
  dismiss
3 candidate
  applicant
4 apply
5 recruit
6 punctual
7 employer
8 astute
9 retire

Language review

1 What does Mark do for a living?
2 Where does Mark work?
3 When did he start working there?
4 Does he enjoy his job?
5 What does he do in his spare time?
6 How much does he earn?
7 Does he have any perks?
8 Does he get a bonus?
9 Why did he leave his last job?
10 What did he do?

B

1 What's your name?
2 What do you do?
3 How long have you been working there?
4 Where were you born?
5 How do you travel to work?
6 How long does it take?
7 What are your hobbies?
8 Why did you leave your last company?
9 What interests you most about your current job?
10 What do your colleagues say about you?

Writing

1 F 2 F 3 T 4 F 5 T 6 T 7 F 8 F

1 Mr. Bolen
2 inform
3 unsuccessful
4 candidates
5 high
6 impressed
7 experience
8 position
9 would
10 take
11 thank
12 wish
13 success
14 sincerely

	an application form	a covering letter	a CV / resume	an interview	new staff	a post	a probationary period	a reference	a short-list	a vacancy
to advertise						✔				✔
to attend				✔						
to complete	✔						✔			
to draw up									✔	
to fill in / out	✔									
to hire					✔					
to submit	✔		✔							
to supply								✔		
to write		✔								

Good news
delighted to confirm
Bad news
regret to inform you that

6 Trade

Vocabulary

1 d   2 c   3 a   4 b   5 e

B

1 CIF	4 FAS
2 CF	5 ex-works
3 FOB	

C

1 **Documents**
   bill of exchange
   certificate of value and origin
   import licence
   letter of credit
   sales invoice

2 **Means of transport**
   air freight
   rail freight
   sea freight

3 **Packaging**
   barrels   drums
   containers   sacks
   crates

4 **Payments**
   import duty
   insurance premium
   surcharge

5 **People**
   customs officer
   freight forwarding agent
   insurance broker

6 **Places**
   docks
   port of arrival
   port of origin
   warehouse

Language review

1 provided that
2 unless
3 Unless
4 unless
5 provided that
6 So long as
7 Unless
8 as long as
9 provided that
10 provided that

1 make	4 reach / meet / achieve
2 expect / want	5 reserve
3 meet / achieve	6 willing / prepared

7 take / accept
8 reasonable / fine

Writing

A

1 following	4 Delivery:
2 consignment	5 warehouse
3 cases	6 at sight

7 shipping documents
8 settle
9 alternative

7 Innovation

Vocabulary

	designs	ideas	problems	research	solutions	tests
analyse		✔	✔			
brainstorm		✔				
carry out				✔		✔
come up with		✔			✔	
conduct						✔
develop	✔	✔			✔	
do				✔		✔
find					✔	
patent	✔	✔				
solve			✔			
tackle			✔			

Language review

A

1 The chocolate bar was invented by Jean-Antoine Menier.
2 The newspaper was invented by Abraham Verhoeven in 1605.
3 20% of our workforce are being made redundant.
4 Our head office in Canada is being relocated.
5 The first motor car was produced by Carl Benz in 1884.
6 The first steam ship was built by Patrick Miller in Scotland in 1799.
7 The new proposal was being considered for most of last week.
8 The credit card was introduced in 1950 by Ralph Schneider.
9 The 9.00 am flight to Hong Kong has been cancelled.
10 The problem is being investigated.

B

1 Wine is made in France. It is not produced in Norway.
2 Coffee is grown in ...
3 Perfume is manufactured in ...
4 Whisky is distilled / made in ...
5 Toyota cars are assembled / built / manufactured in ...
6 Oil is found in ...
7 Cigars are made in ...
8 Peanuts are grown in ...
9 Rice is grown in ...
10 Ships are built in ...
11 Gold is mined in ...

1 was devised
2 was exploited
3 was invented
4 was reported
5 is produced
6 was found
7 is now grown
8 are ground
9 is used
10 was opened
11 was followed
12 are picked
13 are put
14 are placed
15 are then washed
16 (are) spread out
17 are put
18 have been roasted
19 are ground
20 is made

D

1 He is being made redundant.
2 It is being relocated.
3 It was / has been changed.
4 It has been devalued.
5 He / She has been taken ill.
6 It has been stolen.
7 It has been rearranged.

Writing

A

1 on behalf of
2 the quality of your products
3 Please
4 Could you also provide
5 place a substantial order

B

1 ✔
2 by
3 range
4 leaflet
5 complete / entire
6 the
7 supply
8 quantity
9 of
10 discount
11 ✔
12 made
13 ✔
14 you
15 details
16 ✔
17 an
18 ✔
19 be
20 ✔
21 receiving
22 ✔

8 Organisation

Vocabulary

1 C   2 B   3 D   4 A

1 1   2 4   3 3   4 2

1 –   2 b   3 b   4 –   5 a   6 b
7 –   8 a   9 a   10 b   11 a

Language review

Business	consultant	leaders	trip		
Management	consultant	gurus	teams		
Office	block	equipment	hours	staff	
Sales	department	drive	staff	talk	tax
	teams	trip			

B

1 b   2 c   3 a   4 a   5 b   6 c   7 a   8 c   9 a

9 Money

Vocabulary

Currency	Country	Nationality
dollar	United States	American
drachma	Greece	Greek
pound	United Kingdom	British
rand	South Africa	South African
rouble	Russia	Russian
won	South Korea	South Korean
yen	Japan	Japanese
yuan	China	Chinese

B

1 $ 2 $ 3 £   4 £   5 $ 6 £   7 $ 8 $ 9 $

C

1 F   2 T   3 T   4 F   5 T   6 F   7 F   8 F   9 T   10 T
11 F   12 T

Language review

	Infinitive	Past simple	Past participle	Noun
1	decline	declined	declined	a decline
2	decrease	decreased	decreased	a decrease
3	drop	dropped	dropped	a drop
4	fall	fell	fallen	a fall
5	fluctuate	fluctuated	fluctuated	a fluctuation
6	gain	gained	gained	a gain
7	improve	improved	improved	an improvement
8	increase	increased	increased	an increase
9	jump	jumped	jumped	a jump
10	level off	levelled off	levelled off	a levelling off
11	lose	lost	lost	a loss
12	plummet	plummeted	plummeted	–
13	recover	recovered	recovered	a recovery
14	rise	rose	risen	a rise
15	rocket	rocketed	rocketed	–
16	stabilise	stabilised	stabilised	a stabilisation

	Type of change				
	small	large	very large	fast	slow
considerably		✔			
dramatically			✔	✔	
enormously			✔		
gradually					✔
quickly				✔	
rapidly				✔	
sharply				✔	
significantly		✔			
slightly	✔				
substantially		✔			
vastly			✔		

Writing

1 Terms of Reference
2 Procedure
3 Findings
4 Conclusion
5 Recommendations

B

1 commissioned
2 based on
3 submitted by
4 together with a recommendation
5 gathered

C

1 original concept
2 well researched
3 proceed to the next stage

D

1 at the request of
2 it contains my suggestions / recommendations / some ideas have been given
3 was required / was to be submitted
4 have great market potential / greatly increase sales / would be very profitable
5 done some research / carried out some research

6 should develop / should manufacture
7 should present ideas
8 More information is required / needed

10 Ethics

Vocabulary

See table at the bottom of this page.

B

accuse somebody of offering bribes
charge somebody with breaking guidelines
prosecute somebody for selling dangerous goods
sentence somebody to three years in prison
sue somebody for damages

defraud
discredit
misinform
mislead
misrepresent
mistreat
misuse
overbook
overcharge
overprice
undermine

defraud a company / consumers / customers / people
discredit a company / people
misinform consumers / customers / people / staff
mislead consumers / customers / people / staff
misrepresent facts
mistreat consumers / customers / people / staff
misuse information
overbook seats
overcharge consumers / customers / people
overprice goods
undermine confidence / people

D

1 b   2 c   3 a   4 c   5 b

Language review

a 1   b 8   c 10   d 7   e 9   f 6   g 2   h 4   i 3   j 5

	companies	contracts	crimes	documents	laws	products	regulations	sanctions
boycott	✔					✔		
breach		✔					✔	
break					✔		✔	✔
commit			✔					
falsify				✔				
impose								✔

1	had spent	11	had used
2	realised	12	had risen
3	faced / was facing	13	(had) bought
4	had been / was	14	(had) seemed
5	had	15	(had) crashed
6	was making	16	telephoned
7	(had) met	17	apologised
8	(had) advised	18	had had
9	had given	19	replied
10	(had) told		

Writing

1 Why throw away paper?
How about giving it to us?
We will collect ... and save you the cost of disposing of it yourself.

2 a flexible service
saving you time and money
showing that you care about the environment
enhancing your image with your customers
offering you a tailor-made service, with collections at your convenience

3 with over 20 years' experience
See our list of satisfied customers and testimonies to our outstanding service

4 Why not try our one-month trial period, under no obligation?
You'll get your money back if you are not fully satisfied.
Discounts of up to 20% are available for long-term contracts.
call us now on ...

11 Change

Vocabulary

1 N 2 P 3 P 4 N 5 N 6 P
7 P 8 P 9 P 10 N 11 P 12 N

company loyalty
job security / insecurity
resistance to change
threat of redundancy
progress report

1 relocation
2 insecurity, morale, team spirit
3 delayering, downsizing, re-engineering, restructuring

Language review

1 They agreed that he / she was right on that point.
2 He warned her to be careful of very rapid change.
3 He reminded her that people dislike change.
4 He offered to help with the new rota.
5 He suggested using a courier service to speed things up.
6 He advised her to speak to the boss first.
7 He emphasised that it is/was important to talk about change.
8 He pointed out that there are/were several problems with the new location.
9 He explained that the new reporting system worked in the following way.
10 He recommended making changes in the summer / that changes be made in the summer.

1 Why do you want the job?
2 How long did you work in your previous job?
3 Can you use the latest software?
4 How old are you?
5 What do you do in your spare time?
6 Do you have / Have you got a clean driving licence?
7 Do you speak any foreign languages?
8 How do you feel about all the changes in your previous company?
9 Do you smoke?

Writing

AGENDA
for the management meeting
16 June, 11 am in room 18

1 Review of the product range
2 Our agent in Hungary
3 Selection of candidates for the course at Insead
4 Presentation of new logo designs
5 Date of next meeting
6 Any other business

Agenda item/ Action agreed	Who will do it	When and how they will report back
3 Oscar and Rosemarie selected for Insead seminar	Dominic to announce	–
2 Review agent's performance; ask him / her for an explanation	Pieter	Short report by the end of the month
1 Conduct a study of all products; identify unprofitable ones	Lois	Oral report at the next meeting
4 Use another firm of design consultants	Susan	Draw up a list of three firms by the end of the week

12 Stategy

Vocabulary

1 b **2** c **3** f **4** e **5** a **6** d **7** g

1 form an alliance
2 penetrate the market
3 take a stake
4 look for a partner
5 reach an agreement
6 launch a bid
7 set an objective

1 g **2** d **3** f **4** b **5** a **6** e **7** h **8** c

Language review

	for	on	to	no preposition
account	✔		✔	
agree		✔	✔	
apply	✔		✔	
belong			✔	
complain			✔	
depend		✔		
discuss				✔
enter				✔
look	✔		✔	
meet				✔
pay	✔			
phone				✔
rely		✔		
talk			✔	
tell				✔
wait	✔	✔		
write	✔	✔	✔	

B

1 Would you phone ~~to~~ Johnson Consultants regarding the joint venture agreement?
2 I agree that we should enter ~~into~~ the Spanish market by the end of the year.
3 The home market accounts **for** 60% of their sales.
4 We cannot continue to depend **on** one product.
5 We're relying **on** your support at the board meeting.
6 We seem to agree **on** the need for an alliance with a German firm.
7 We need to discuss ~~about~~ this further.
8 We are looking **for** a new partner in Eastern Europe.
9 We'll wait **for** your answer on the takeover proposal.
10 They are complaining **to** the management because they were not consulted about the take-over.

Writing

1 the proposed merger with Unibank
2 Stephen Wade
3 12 February
4 to summarise the advantages and disadvantages of a possible merger with Unibank
5 15 March
6 From various sources:
Unibank's publicity material
annual reports
financial publications
material from the Internet
confidential study by City Consultants

3 As requested in your memo of 12 February
4 my report summarising the advantages and disadvantages of a possible merger with Unibank
5 You asked for the report to be submitted by 15 March.
6 I have collected information from various sources including …

Modal verbs

13 Culture

Vocabulary

1 b c
2 a c
3 b c
4 a b
5 a b
6 a c

Language review

1 I would like to ~~can~~ go abroad more.
2 She must ~~to~~ do it now.
3 You can**not have** the cheque now.
4 I **had to** go into the office last weekend.
5 I'm sorry to **have to** tell you this.
6 I **can't** type.
7 Could you tell~~ing~~ me the time.

B

Company A should not have served pork to a group of Muslims.
Company B should have sent an older negotiator.
Company C should not have started the negotiation by announcing their deadlines.

Writing

A

1 from	8 on
2 in	9 in
3 for	10 for
4 for	11 in
5 at	12 in
6 from / on	13 for
7 on	14 in

B

1 Ms Driessen
2 Thank you very much
3 on the date you suggest
4 I would prefer to speak
5 an excellent presentation
6 mentioned
7 This seems rather low
8 provide me with
9 Finally
10 could you possibly send me
11 I'm looking forward to seeing
12 Yours sincerely

D

To express his thanks
... thank you for your hospitality ...
It was most kind of you to invite me and Jenny ...
Once again, my thanks for your efforts on our behalf.

To show that he and his wife really enjoyed the trip
You helped to make our visit very memorable.
Jenny enjoyed immensely visiting some of your department stores ...
I will never forget the trips to ...
It was a pleasure to meet you all.

14 Leadership

Vocabulary

A

1 a 2 f 3 j 4 e 5 d 6 i
7 b 8 c 9 g 10 h 11 k

B

1 objectives	6 motivate
2 strategies	7 activities
3 decisions	8 dealing with
4 measure	9 delegate
5 orders	10 information

Language review

1 A scientist who invented a new drug to treat AIDS became the head of the company.
2 The company which fired its Sales Director was taken to court.
3 The management consultants who advised me were not very good.
4 Our computer system, which cost over £1m, breaks down frequently.

5 Sven Andersson, who joined as Chief Executive last year, has impressed everybody.
6 The team leader, who comes from Brazil, speaks several languages.
7 Our head office, which is located in Zurich, is very costly to run.
8 Our Managing Director, who was recruited from outside the firm, has been very successful.

B

My favourite boss was a woman **who** was younger than me. She had not had a formal university education. She went straight from school to a travel firm in Cardiff, **which** is the capital of Wales.

The firm, **which** organised business travel and holidays for top executives, was one of the biggest travel firms in the UK. One of the top executives, **who** met her when she was organising his firm's company trip, was really impressed with her. He hired her as his PA, **which** meant she was able to accompany him all round the world. When he retired she succeeded him as Chief Executive and the company went from strength to strength.

She was a leader **who** was fair but firm and was willing to deal with difficult issues immediately. Her employees, **who** all spoke very highly of her, were very motivated. She had a clear strategy for the business **which** her staff understood and fully supported. She was also compassionate and her secretary, **who** had worked with her for many years, greatly admired her. She was married and had two children. Her husband, **who** worked with her in the business, described her as a superwoman. 'She has enormous energy **which** enables her to work harder than other people,' he said. 'She hasn't missed a single day through illness.'

Writing

A

1 Special skills	9 Education
2 Personal details	10 Work experience
3 Personal details	11 Work experience
4 Qualifications	12 Personal details
5 Special skills	13 Special skills
6 Interests and achievements	14 Qualifications
7 Interests and achievements	15 Qualifications
8 Education	16 Referees

B

1, 2 and 6

D

1 developing
2 co-ordinating / organising
3 negotiating
4 monitoring / reviewing
5 setting up / organising / developing / reviewing
6 extensive experience / a proven track record
7 under pressure
8 delegate
9 creative
10 dynamic / energetic
11 efficient
12 fluent

15 Competition

Vocabulary

competitive advantage
lower costs
market leader
rival firms
unique benefits

1 competitive advantage
2 lower costs
3 unique benefits
4 rival firms
5 market leader

1 cut-throat	5 fierce
2 keen	6 unfair
3 strong	7 intense
4 tough	8 free

1 g 2 d 3 b 4 h 5 f 6 e 7 a 8 c

deregulation
cartel, corner the market, monopoly, price fixing

Language review

1 are … going	6 arrive
2 will be / is	7 will hire / are hiring
3 are … going	8 drive / driving
4 do … fly / are … flying	9 will be / is
5 leaves / is leaving	10 will keep

1 I'm seeing; he'll recognise
2 It's going to; We won't sell
3 are you doing
4 will go up; are you going to do
5 leaves

Writing

1 confirm	5 call
2 prefer	6 suggest
3 discussed	7 attends
4 do	8 getting through

I'm afraid
I'm really sorry but …
Sorry for …
Could I suggest …
Would 2 pm suit you?
It's the least I can do.
Once again, my apologies …

16 Quality

Vocabulary

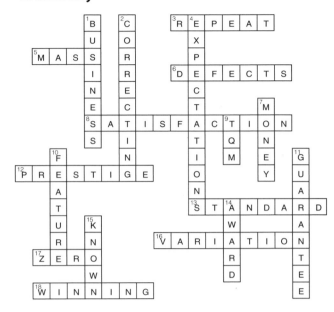

Language review

1 of	5 for
2 on	6 in / during
3 by	7 at
4 in / during	

Writing

B

1 invoice	4 settle
2 cheque	5 latest
3 outstanding	

C

1 statement	6 cleared
2 overdue	7 settle
3 payment	8 within
4 understand	9 matter
5 appreciate it	10 immediate

D

2, 1, 3

Talk business

Introduction

1 Group 1: cost, job, lost, offer
   Group 2: most, post
   Explanation: The *o* in Group 2 is pronounced as in *flow*, not as in *loss*.

2 Group 1: keycard, market
   Group 2: knock-on, know-how
   Explanation: The letter *k* at the beginning of a word is not pronounced if it is followed by *n*.

3 Group 1: ago, global, growth
   Group 2: regional, strategy
   Explanation: In Group 2 the *g* is pronounced as in the keyword *joint*.

4 Group 1: adjust, plunge
   Group 2: consumer, securities
   Explanation: In Group 1 the letter *u* is pronounced as in the keyword *money*.

5 Group 1: boom, borrow
   Group 2: climb, debt
   Explanation: In Group 2 the *b* is silent, i.e. it is not pronounced.

6 Group 1: April, inflation, rate, taken
   Group 2: market, partner, past
   Explanation: In Group 1 the letter *a* is pronounced as a diphthong, as in the keyword *sale*.

7 Group 1: announce, discount
   Group 2: group, through
   Explanation: In Group 1 the letters *ou* are pronounced as a diphthong as in the keyword *account*.

1 Globalisation

Individual sounds

 See audio script 1.1.

Connected speech

 See audio script 1.4.

Stress and intonation

See audio script 1.5.

Telephoning

1 Heavey
2 361 1363 22 67
3 020 441 595
4 Meynell
   PR2 8BS
5 de Vuyst
   Maes

1 to / in
2 for
3 back /back
4 to / by / at

Socialising 1

 See audio script 1.8 for intonation.

1 B agrees
2 B agrees strongly
3 B agrees strongly

2 Brands

Individual sounds

/d/	/t/	/ɪd/
complained informed received reorganised	finished increased worked	decided expanded invited

Stress and intonation

 See audio script 2.4.

First-time meetings

1 d   2 b   3 c   4 a

1 met   5 realise
2 was   6 work
3 flew   7 tell
4 been   8 See

Informal conversation

8, 1, 5, 4, 6, 3, 7, 2

Sample answers
1 Good morning / afternoon.
2 What have you been doing (since we last met)?
3 I'm afraid I must hurry.
4 Could you phone tomorrow.
5 Goodbye.

3 Travel

Individual sounds

1 a **2** a **3** b **4** b **5** a **6** a

Connected speech

 See audio script 3.3.

Stress and intonation

 See audio script 3.5.

Asking for agreement or confirmation

	↗	↘
1		✔
2	✔	
3	✔	
4	✔	
5		✔
6		✔

Useful phrases

A

1 on
2 over
3 in
4 in
5 through
6 in

1 d **2** c **3** e **4** b **5** f **6** a

B

1 through the grapevine
2 on the same wavelength
3 in the same boat
4 in the balance
5 in a nutshell
6 over the moon

4 Advertising

Individual sounds

A *See audio script 4.1.*

B

–a–	–ay–	–ai–	–ea–
changes	May	details	great
latest	pay	paid	
made	payment		
Rachel			
sales			
unable			

Connected speech

1 7 **2** 8 **3** 9 **4** 12

Stress and intonation

 See audio script 4.5 for intonation.

1 B agrees
2 B disagrees
3 B agrees

Starting presentations

Mamba	Deltelcom
1 h	**1** b
2 c	**2** d
3 f	**3** g
4 e	**4** a

5 Employment

Individual sounds

B

	/ɒ/	/əʊ/
1	job	
2	shop	
3		sold
4	offer	
5		open
6		wrote

Stress and intonation

Ooo	oOo	ooO
applicant	appearance	personnel
benefits	dismissal	
candidate	promotion	
company	retirement	
interview		

Managing meetings

1 c **2** a **3** b **4** f **5** d **6** e
7 e **8** c **9** d **10** f **11** b **12** a

Asking for repetition

 See audio script 5.6 for sample answers.

6 Trade

Individual sounds

1 /uː/ 4 /ʊ/
2 /ʊ/ 5 /uː/
3 /uː/ 6 /ʊ/

Connected speech

B *See audio script 6.3.*

Stress and intonation

A

1 b 2 d 3 d

C *See audio script 6.6.*

Negotiating

A

1 order 5 insurance
2 terms 6 discount
3 costs 7 delivery
4 shipping 8 letter

B

Supplier: 1, 2, 6 and 7
Buyer: 3, 4, 5 and 8

C

if; on condition that; provided that; so long as; as long as; (not) unless

D

1 2 and 3
2 1 and 4
See Market Leader *page 136 , Conditions, points 1 and 2.*

E

1 No 2 No 3 Yes 4 Yes 5 No

7 Innovation

Individual sounds

A

1 d 2 b 3 c 4 a

B

–or–	–ear–	–er–	–ir–	–ere–	–ur–
work	heard	commercial	first	were	further
world	research	refer			
word	earn	personal			
		expert			

Stress and intonation

B *See audio script 7.4.*

Making presentations

B *See audio script 7.6.*

Insisting tactfully

B *See audio script 7.7.*

8 Organisation

Individual sounds

A

1 b 2 a 3 d

B

–o–	–u–	–ou–	–oe–
money	unlimited	encourage	does
company	bankruptcy		
	public		
	redundant		
	number		
	consultant		

Connected speech

B *See audio script 8.3.*

Stress and intonation

See audio script 8.4

Conversation skills

A

There is no continuity in the conversation. In order to keep the conversation going, comment on the answer to a question you have asked or ask a follow-up question.

B

2, 6, 5, 9, 1, 8, 4, 7, 3

C

Sample answers
1 Hmm …, they say it's one of the best hotels in town.
2 Maybe next time.
3 No, that's all right. We've already ordered one for you.

D *See audio script 8.6.*

9 Money

Individual sounds

	/aʊ/	/əʊ/
1	south	
2		below
3		loan
4		zero
5	allow	
6	thousand	

Stress and intonation

 See audio script 9.5.

Correcting information

 See audio script 9.7.

Describing trends

1 for	5 up
2 at	6 at
3 By	7 in
4 to	

2, 7, 5, 4, 3, 6, 1

10 Ethics

Individual sounds

	/æ/	/ʌ/
1		drunk
2		run
3	rang	
4	sang	

Connected speech

1 weak, strong	3 weak, strong
2 weak, strong	4 weak, strong

Stress and intonation

1 c 2 b 3 a 4 a 5 b

Problem solving

1 b 2 c 3 d 4 e 5 a

a) <u>How about</u> telling him it's not on? Nepotism is a thing of the past, isn't it?

b) <u>Have you thought of</u> confronting him with the issue? He may have genuine health problems.

c) <u>I suggest you</u> check his personal file first to see if he's ever been accused of sexual harassment.

d) <u>I think we should</u> tell her not to speak to anybody. The issue is far too serious.

e) <u>If I were you,</u> I'd give her another chance. Honestly, she doesn't look the type of person who'd cook the books.

Tactful suggestions

1 b 2 b

 See audio script 10.6.

11 Change

Individual sounds

	/v/	/w/
1		one
2	of	
3	favourite	
4	venues	
5	Vic	
6		was
7		working
8		with
9	executive	
10	Vesna	
11	vision	
12	everybody	

Connected speech

See audio script 11.4.

Stress and intonation

See audio script 11.5.

Agreeing and disagreeing 1

1 f 2 e 3 c 4 a 5 b 6 d

a) <u>I agree with you</u> up to a point, but don't forget that their capacity is being cut drastically.

b) I'm afraid <u>I can't agree with you</u> there. That's a lot more than we can afford.

c) <u>That's right.</u> In fact, they're soaring.

d) <u>That's out of the question,</u> I'm afraid. It's far too inefficient. We should close it down.

e) <u>You're absolutely right.</u> I think we should strengthen our presence there.

f) Yes, <u>I'm in total agreement with you</u> there. We need to make our packaging more attractive.

Asking for clarification

1 e **2** a **3** d **4** b **5** c

1 Can I just ask a question at this point? You were telling us why the economy in Asia and South America remains difficult.
2 Sorry, could I stop you there for a moment? I'd like to go back to something you said earlier about your ability to deliver high profits regardless of market conditions.
3 If I may interrupt, there's something I'm not sure I fully understood. You said you expected a 10% increase in sales next year.
4 If it's all right, there's a question I'd like to ask. When you were describing the plans for the restructuring of the Luxembourg plant, you hinted that redundancies were not unlikely.
5 Sorry for cutting in on you. You said you were in favour of a limited licensing agreement.

a) Could you be a little more specific about what you mean by 'high profits' and tell us exactly how much pre-tax profit you expect?
b) Could you tell us a bit more about the consequences of those plans and if possible specify how many people might be in danger of being laid off?
c) Could you specify what you mean by 'limited' please?
d) Could you elaborate on that and explain how you think such an increase can be achieved considering that the market in the region seems to have come to a halt?
e) Could you go over what you said about the Far East again, please, and tell us what the prospects might be in the next two years?

12 Strategy

Individual sounds

	/ɔː/	/əʊ/
1		whole
2	more	
3		go
4		those
5		approached
6	broad	
7	or	
8		growing
9	important	
10		control

Connected speech

There is a link when the next word starts with a vowel sound. *See audio script 12.3.*

Stress and intonation

See audio script 12.4.

Sounding decisive

 See audio script 12.6.

D *See audio script 12.8.*

13 Culture

Individual sounds

–ea–	–e–	–ee
team deal reasons	Japanese strategic	agree three

Connected speech

There is a link when the next word starts with a vowel sound. *See audio script 13.3.*

Stress and intonation

1 doubt / reservation
2 doubt / reservation
3 enthusiasm

Socialising 2

A

1 C **2** C

B *See audio script 13.7 for sample answers.*

1 Yes **2** No **3** Yes **4** Yes **5** No

Adding emphasis

See audio script 13.8 for sample answers.

14 Leadership

Individual sounds

B

	/θ/	/ð/
1	wealth	
2		that
3		together
4	breadth	
5		their
6		father
7		with
8	thing	
9	three	
10	thrive	

Connected speech

(A)

1 8 **2** 7 **3** 6 **4** 8 **5** 13

(B) *See audio script 14.4.*

Stress and intonation

See audio script 14.5 for stressed syllables.

1 c **2** b **3** b **4** b **5** c

Saying what you mean

(A) *See audio script 14.6.*

(B)

1 a **2** b **3** d **4** c **5** f **6** e

Giving explanations

(B)

1 which
2 who
3 which
4 who

15 Competition

Individual sounds

(A)

1 c **2** c **3** a **4** c **5** a **6** a

(B)

1 breadth; heavy; threat
2 dealer; leader
3 heard
4 real

Connected speech

See audio script 15.3.

Stress and intonation

See audio script 15.4.

Making an appointment

(A) *See audio script 15.5 for sample answers.*

Agreeing and disagreeing 2

(B) *See audio script 15.7 for sample answers.*

(C) *See audio script 15.8 for sample answers.*

16 Quality

Individual sounds

(B) *See audio script 16.2.*

Connected speech

See audio script 16.3 for sample answer.

Stress and intonation

1 c **2** b **3** d **4** a

Polite requests in meetings

(B)

1 b **2** b **3** a **4** b **5** a **6** a **7** a

Dealing with problems

1 computer
2 fax, photocopier
3 telephone
4 computer
5 fax, photocopier
6 all
7 drinks machine, lift
8 computer, drinks machine, lift, photocopier

a 3
b 1, 4, 6
c 2, 6
d 5
e 1, 2, 6, 7
f 1, 4, 6
g 2, 6, 7, 8
h 1, 2, 6, 8

Introduction

The sounds of English

Vowel sounds

/ɪ/	'image	/ɔː/	launch
/iː/	team	/ʊ/	full
/e/	sell	/uː/	re'duce
/æ/	cash	/ʌ/	'money
/ɑː/	chart	/ɜː/	term
/ɒ/	loss	/ə/	'modern, ca'reer

Diphthongs

/eɪ/	sale	/əʊ/	flow
/aɪ/	price	/ɪə/	dear
/ɔɪ/	oil	/eə/	share
/aʊ/	a'ccount	/ʊə/	tour

Consonants

Voiceless		Voiced	
/p/	pay	/b/	buy
/s/	sell	/z/	goods
/t/	telephone	/d/	deal
/ʃ/	option	/ʒ/	decision
/k/	copy	/g/	global
/tʃ/	cheap	/dʒ/	joint
/f/	file	/v/	venture
/θ/	think	/ð/	this
/l/	loss	/h/	head
/r/	rise	/m/	media
/j/	year	/n/	net
/w/	win	/ŋ/	branding

1 Globalisation

1.1

1 It's lighter and smaller.
2 It's much bigger than Hong Kong.
3 The US dollar is much stronger than many other currencies.
4 The Moscow underground is cheaper than the one in London.

1.2

1 Prices in Moscow are among the highest in Europe.
2 Cleveland is one of the cleanest cities in North America.

1.3

1 Their prices are as low as ours.

2 Ireland isn't as large as Sweden.

1.4

1 They'll have to deal with the problem as soon as possible.

2 The new photocopier is as unreliable as the old one.

1.5

1 Nine o'clock already! I have to ring up the Sales Manager.
2 I didn't manage to get through to him.
3 I've forgotten his number. Could you look it up in the phone book for me, please?
4 He was asking about the sales report, but then we were cut off.
5 I'll try to call back later.

1.6

1 A: Could you tell me your name?
   B: Certainly. It's Tom Heavey.
      That's H-E-A-V-E-Y.
2 A: Could I possibly have your home number just in case?
   B: Of course. It's three-six-one for Hungary, and then one-three-six-three, twenty-two, sixty-seven.
3 A: I'm afraid I didn't get your fax number.
   B: It's oh-two-oh, four-four-one, five-nine-five.
4 A: And what's your address, Mr Andrews?
   B: It's 22 Meynell Drive, Preston.
   A: How do you spell Meynell?
   B: M-E-Y-N-E-L-L.
   A: And it's Preston, you said. Do you know the post code?
   B: Yes, it's PR2 8BS.
5 A: Could you spell your surname for me?
   B: Sure. It's in two words: D-E with a small D, and then V-U-Y-S-T.
   A: And could I have your address?
   B: 15 rue Maes, Brussels.
   A: Sorry, how exactly do you spell the street name?
   B: That's M-A-E-S.
   A: Thank you.

1.7

1 A: Lovely day, isn't it?
   B: Yes, beautiful.

2 A: Lovely day, isn't it?
   B: Yes, beautiful.

1.8

1 A: Beautiful day, isn't it?
   B: Yes, wonderful.

2 A: Busy morning, isn't it?
   B: Yes, hectic.

3 A: Interesting, this article on globalisation, isn't it?
   B: Yes, fascinating.

2 Brands

2.1
joined; launched; visited.

2.2
complained; decided; expanded; finished; increased; informed; invited; received; reorganised; worked.

2.3
1 She worked in the sales department for eight years.

2 She became Head of Sales last August.

3 Our share price has increased sharply because of our excellent results.

2.4
com.pe.ti.tion; com.pe.ti.tor; com.pete
dis.tri.bu.tion; dis.tri.bu.tor; dis.tri.bute
pro.mo.tion; pro.mo.ter; pro.mote
re.search; re.search.er; re.search
con.sump.tion; con.su.mer; con.sume
ad.ver.tise.ment; ad.ver.ti.ser; ad.ver.tise

2.5
F = Fiona, DO = David Olsen, FA = Frances Atkinson

F: David, have you met our new Marketing Manager, Frances Atkinson? Frances, this is David Olsen, from CBK Ljubljana.
DO: How do you do?
FA: Pleased to meet you. How was your trip?
DO: Fine, thanks. I flew Swissair this time. And the weather was splendid.
FA: Yes, we're lucky. It's been like this for almost a week now. Which hotel are you staying at?
DO: The Calypso, as usual. Friendly service, amazing facilities and just a ten-minute walk away.
FA: Oh, I didn't realise you'd been here before.
DO: Yes, three times, actually. I used to work as a consultant for your HR department.
FA: How interesting! I suppose that was before April 1997, then. That's when I joined the company.
DO: Yes, that was back in 1992–93. HR was being completely restructured. It was all very exciting.
FA: Hmm …, you must tell me more about it over lunch.
DO: Yes. It's been nice talking to you. See you later.
FA: Bye for now.

2.6
G = Greg, D = Dilek

G: Hello, Dilek. How are things going?
D: Very well thanks, Greg. And how are you?
G: Fine thanks. Haven't seen you for a while. What have you been up to?
D: It's been rather hectic at work, actually. Six new contracts in ten days.
G: Wow, well done!
D: I'm in a bit of a rush, I'm afraid. Give us a ring tomorrow. All right?
G: Yeah. I'll be in touch. Cheers!
D: See you!

3 Travel

3.1
1 They'll do it for you.
2 We'll travel by air.
3 I go to visit them on Tuesday.
4 You tell them everything.
5 They'll buy as much as possible.
6 We'll make all the reservations.

3.2
1 You can't give everybody the exact seat they want.
2 Most passengers were homeward-bound commuters.

3.3
1 I'll be in London next week.
2 It'll cost around five hundred pounds.
3 Can I take this as hand luggage?
4 I thought it was exempt from tax.
5 I'd like a round trip to Boston.

3.4
1 What time do I have to check in?

2 Who will pick her up at the airport?

3.5
1 How much is an open ticket?

2 How long does it take to get to the station?

3 When did you confirm the arrangements?

4 Where will she be going next week?

3.6
1 Surely there's an earlier flight, isn't there?

2 They've booked me into the Astoria again, haven't they?

3.7
1 That could be changed from business to economy, couldn't it?

2 They caught the afternoon flight, didn't they?

3 You want to book a sleeper, don't you?

4 You are on the waiting list, aren't you?

5 She's going to take an earlier flight back, isn't she?

6 You have changed my flight booking, haven't you?

4 Advertising

4.1
sales; sells

1 paper
2 sent
3 best
4 date

4.2
changes; details; great; latest; made; May; paid; pay; payment; Rachel; sales; unable

4.3
1 The delay's caused us great inconvenience.
2 They've come up with some good ideas.
3 So far it's had little impact on sales.
4 It's one of the biggest advertising campaigns we've ever seen.

4.4
1 A: It's a very memorable advert.
   B: Yes.

2 A: This will add value to our products.
   B: Yes.

4.5
1 A: What we need is a product which is really different from our competitors'.
   B: Yes.

2 A: We've always used the best advertising methods.
   B: Yes.

3 A: This will persuade people to choose our products.
   B: Yes.

4.6
1 A: I'm ringing to let you know we still haven't received the details of your advertisement.
   B: I'm sorry to hear they haven't reached you yet. I'll look into the matter straightaway.
2 A: Jonathan Webb here. I checked our ad in the latest issue of *Ambition* magazine. I'm afraid your department has made quite a few serious errors.
   B: I'm very sorry to hear some mistakes have been made, Mr Webb. If you would give me some details I'll take the matter up at once.
3 A: Jonathan Webb speaking. Why was I not informed about the change in positioning? This is the second time this has happened.
   B: I'm terribly sorry to hear you weren't notified. I'll ask Hannah Levy to attend to it immediately.

4.7
Presentation 1
This afternoon, I'm going to talk to you about Mamba, our new wondertoy due to be launched in November.
I'll start off by outlining the unique features of our product, after which I'll report on the results of the market research we carried out in Central and Eastern Europe.

Then, I'll fill you in on the background to the recent changes in our marketing policy.
Last but not least, I shall also bring you up-to-date on the latest developments in our animatronic toy department.

Presentation 2
Good morning ladies and gentlemen. The theme of my presentation is the increased dividend payment that we will propose to the Annual Shareholders' Meeting next month.
I'll begin by giving you an overview of the major strategic moves which have characterised the past six months.
Then, I'll go on to talk you through a detailed breakdown of last year's results.
Finally, I'll summarise the main reasons for the Board of Directors' confidence in Deltelcom and highlight the factors which now make our organisation fully market driven.

5 Employment

5.1
cost; coast
want; won't

5.2
1 job
2 shop
3 sold
4 offer
5 open
6 wrote

5.3
1 The main part of the interview is the CV.
   /meɪm/
2 He wore a light blue shirt at work.
   /laɪp/
3 It's all down to good preparation.
   /gʊp/
4 It happened in Poland and in Britain.
   /ɪm/   /ɪm/
5 Let's get back to the point.
   /gep/
6 It cost him ten pounds fifty.
   /tem/

5.4
appearance; applicant; benefits; candidate; company; dismissal; interview; personnel; promotion; retirement

5.5
1 A: Ms Reid has invited Mr Roberts to lead a training session for us.
   B: Sorry, I didn't get that. Who did you say she's invited?
2 A: The seminar will be held at our head office on 6 July.
   B: Sorry, where will the seminar be held, did you say?
3 A: She says the main topic will be interview techniques.
   B: I'm afraid I didn't quite catch that. What will the main topic be?

5.6
1 A: We can offer him a fee of $200 if he participates in the seminar.
   B: I didn't quite catch that, I'm afraid. How much can we offer him?

2 A: He complained that the hotel had few facilities.
B: Sorry, I didn't get that. What did he complain about?
3 A: They didn't seem interested in building a relationship.
B: What didn't they seem interested in, did you say?
4 A: Our visitors are due to arrive at 9.10 on Monday the 20th.
B: Sorry, I didn't quite catch that. When did you say they are due to arrive?
5 A: I expected Mr Roberts to get back to me about it.
B: I'm afraid I didn't get that. Who did you say you expected to get back to you about it?

6 Trade

6.1
1 value
2 goods
3 future
4 reputable
5 producer
6 distributor

6.2
1 we asked
2 agree on
3 agree a deal
4 they agreed
5 a day or two
6 my assistant

6.3
1 I'm sure they'll agree a deal in a day or two.
2 I asked my assistant to see to it.
3 May or June would be all right, wouldn't it?

6.4
1 a) offer   b) receipt   c) discount (noun)   d) import (noun)
2 a) deliver   b) distribute   c) agreement   d) quantity
3 a) quotas   b) tariffs   c) customs   d) import (verb)

6.5
Their major exports are flowers, seeds, bulbs and cheese.

6.6
1 Their main trading partners are in Germany, Greece, Slovenia and Austria.
2 In her lecture, she talked about tariffs, quotas, dumping and deregulation.
3 Please remember to mention quantity, total value, method of payment and documents required.

6.7
1 If you order within three days, we'll offer a very attractive discount.
2 If you place a large order, we'll give you a 4% discount.
3 If you agreed to pay within a month, we'd let you pay by letter of credit.
4 If you dispatched within a fortnight, we'd cover insurance ourselves.
5 If you cover shipping costs, we'll increase our order.

7 Innovation

7.1
work

1 a) heard   b) commercial   c) first   d) patent
2 a) refer   b) ingenious   c) personal   d) expert
3 a) were   b) further   c) feasible   d) world
4 a) efficient   b) research   c) word   d) earn

7.2
1 Hello everybody!
   /w/
2 How much do you know about those new ideas?
                    /w/   /w/
3 I'd like to answer that question before I go on.
      /w/   /w/
4 You'll have to emphasise two of those points.
      /w/   /w/

7.3
1 A: You should buy a pager, it's very useful.
B: I've got a pager.
2 A: How will we be able to contact you?
B: I've got a pager.

7.4
1 A: Where's R & D?
B: R & D is on the 2nd floor.
2 A: What's on the 2nd floor?
B: R & D is on the 2nd floor.
3 A: Did they buy a mini-bus?
B: No, they hired a mini-bus.
4 A: Did they hire a car?
B: No, they hired a mini-bus.
5 A: How about faxing them?
B: I have sent them a fax.
6 A: You could send them a letter.
B: I have sent them a fax.

7.5
Let's look at these [pause] factors in more [pause] detail. If you look at this pie [pause] chart, you'll see that the sales of our cheaper model went [pause] down by 10% over [pause] the past three months.

7.6
Although there are indications [pause] that the growth of the Hungarian market may have come to a halt, [pause] I firmly believe [pause] that it can easily be counterbalanced [pause] by further increasing exports. [pause]

If you have a look at the figures on the OHT, [pause] you will see that exports accounted for 22%, [pause] and we expect our shares to rise to 27% [pause] by the end of November. [pause]

Let us look first at the main cause [pause] of this dramatic growth in exports. [pause] As you know, [pause] the production of all our chocolate bars and breakfast cereals has been moved [pause] from Estonia and Slovakia [pause] to the south-west of Hungary …

7·7

1 A: Does it matter if we don't notify them today?

 B: I'm afraid they really must be notified today, otherwise they might cancel the order.

2 A: Sorry, we won't be able to repair the printer this week.

 B: It really must be repaired this week, I'm afraid, otherwise the handouts won't be ready for the conference.

3 A: There's no way I can meet them at the airport.

 B: I'm afraid they really must be met at the airport, otherwise they'll be offended.

4 A: I don't think we can confirm our order today.

 B: It really must be confirmed today, I'm afraid, otherwise we'll lose the 3% discount.

5 A: Sorry, I won't be able to translate the contract this week.

 B: I'm afraid it really must be translated this week, otherwise our suppliers will never be able to meet the deadline.

8 Organisation

8.1
money

1 a) company **b)** holiday **c)** unlimited **d)** bankruptcy
2 a) business **b)** public **c)** redundant **d)** encourage
3 a) number **b)** consultant **c)** does **d)** shareholder

8.2

1 their assets

2 for example

3 in favour of

4 her assistant

8.3

1 They were able to relocate their offices before April.

2 In your opinion, are there any other advantages?

3 We need more information about the car industry in the Far East.

4 They were all in favour of making her assistant redundant.

8.4

1 credit card
2 company car
3 board meeting
4 trade barriers
5 profit margin
6 multinational company
7 sole trader
8 end-of-year report
9 net profit
10 free trade

8.5
DK = Danila Kravetz, FA = Frances Atkinson

A: Danila, let me introduce you to Frances Atkinson, our Marketing Manager.

DK: Pleased to meet you. I'm Danila Kravetz from CBK Ljubljana.

FA: Pleased to meet you too. Did you have a good flight?

DK: Yes, thank you, apart from a slight delay at Heathrow, it was a good trip.

FA: A good thing you didn't miss your connecting flight! Erm ... Do you actually live in Ljubljana?

DK: Well, yes, I do, but for over six months now I've been doing a research project. So I've been on tour to various parts of Eastern and Central Europe.

FA: Hmm ..., that sounds interesting. And how about your research?

DK: Well, basically, my objective was to assess the markets for our new products.

FA: I'd be extremely interested to go through your research results with you. Do you think we could do that first thing this afternoon?

8.6

A: What's your name?

B: Heather Northcott.

A: Are you English?

B: I'm Irish, actually.

A: And where do you live?

B: In Reading.

A: What's Reading like?

B: It's not terribly exciting, to be honest.

9 Money

9.1
now; no

9.2

1 south
2 below
3 loan
4 zero
5 allow
6 thousand

9.3

1 Other indices were also positive.
2 They said the fall was in line with market expectations.
3 Bangkok Bank was the most active stock.
4 Leading Internet stocks were boosted by a series of ratings changes.
5 Local investors were awaiting news of the fate of the Commerce Bank.

9.4

1 A: Who did you meet this morning?

 B: I met Olga this morning.

2 A: When did you meet Olga?

 B: I met Olga this morning.

9.5

1 A: How do they feel about the profits?

 B: They're worried about the profits.

2 A: What are they worried about?

 B: They're worried about the profits.

3 A: Our next meeting is in October. I'd very much like you to chair it.

 B: I'm afraid I'm going to France in October.

4 A: When you're in Paris this summer, don't miss Kate's training seminar.

B: I'm afraid I'm going to France in October.

9.6
1 A: The shares rose 50 cents to 22.30.
B: That's not quite right. They rose <u>sixty</u> cents.
2 A: The shares rose 60 cents to 22.40.
B: I'm afraid that's not correct. They rose to twenty-two point <u>thirty</u>.
3 A: The shares rose to 24.30.
B: That's not quite right, I'm afraid. They rose to twenty-<u>two</u> point thirty.

9.7
1 A: The bank took DM 3.7 bn in risk provisions to cover property losses in the second quarter of the year.
B: I'm afraid that's not correct. The property losses were in the <u>first</u> quarter of the year.
2 A: The bank took DM 3.3 bn in risk provisions to cover property losses in the first quarter of the year.
B: It seems you haven't got all your figures right. They took DM 3.<u>7</u> bn in risk provisions.
3 A: The bank took DM 2.7 bn in risk provisions to cover property losses in the first quarter of the year.
B: That's not quite right, I'm afraid. They took DM 3.7 bn in risk provisions.

9.8
First, I suggest we have a look at this graph.
It shows last year's sales figures, all expressed in euros. We made a reasonable start at 1.7 million and, rather unexpectedly, sales went up moderately till the end of the first quarter.
This was followed by a drop, owing to a poor sales promotion campaign for our new range of products as well as serious distribution difficulties.
By the end of July, however, we had already recovered.
Sales started to take off at the beginning of August, to reach a record high by the end of December.
We'll be looking at the reasons for this spectacular recovery in a moment.

10 Ethics

10.1
began; begun

10.2
1 drunk
2 run
3 rang
4 sang

10.3
was	/wɒz/	was	/wəz/
were	/wɜː/	were	/wə/
had	/hæd/	had	/həd/
has	/hæz/	has	/həz/
have	/hæv/	have	/həv/

10.4
1 A: Were they really employing people illegally?
B: Yes, they were.

2 A: Was he using the office phone for private purposes?
B: Well, yeah, it seems that he was.
3 A: Had they been prosecuted before?
B: They had, actually. Back in 1997.
4 A: They've been accepting bribes.
B: Have they really?

10.5
1 **a)** trustworthy **b)** ethical **c)** illegal
2 **a)** bribery **b)** evasion **c)** laundering
3 **a)** deceit **b)** devious **c)** sentence
4 **a)** burgle **b)** commit **c)** accuse
5 **a)** espionage **b)** corruption **c)** honesty

10.6
1 Shouldn't we talk to him first?
2 Wouldn't it be better to let her know today?
3 Couldn't we postpone making a decision?
4 Aren't they too expensive?
5 Hadn't we better cancel the deal?
6 Don't we have to tell them the truth about the bribes?
7 Won't they be embarrassed if we mention tax evasion?

11 Change

11.1
of; one

11.2
1 one		**7** working
2 of		**8** with
3 favourite		**9** executive
4 venues		**10** Vesna
5 Vic		**11** vision
6 was		**12** everybody

11.3
1 It's one of my favourite venues.
2 Vic was working with the new Chief Executive.
3 Vesna explained her vision to everybody.

11.4
1 Would you like to begin?
2 I really can't agree with you there.
3 Let's move on to the next item on the agenda.
4 How do you feel about that?
5 Could you explain that a bit more clearly?

11.5
We <u>want</u> to be a company that is <u>constantly</u> re<u>new</u>ing itself, <u>leaving</u> the <u>past</u> be<u>hind</u>, a<u>dapting</u> to <u>change</u>. <u>Manage</u>ments that hang on to <u>weak</u>ness for what<u>ever</u> reason – tradition, sentiment, or their <u>own</u> management weakness – <u>won't</u> be a<u>round</u> in the future.

11.6
1 A: Quality has a lot to do with appearance.
B: Yes, I'm in total agreement with you there. We need to make our packaging more attractive.
2 A: I still see that region as a very significant market.
B: You're absolutely right. I think we should strengthen our presence there.

3 A: Our net profits are still up.
 B: That's right. In fact, they're soaring.
4 A: I think the companies to watch are the car manufacturers.
 B: I agree with you up to a point, but don't forget that their capacity is being cut drastically.
5 A: So what I suggest is that we give them a 5% increase.
 B: I'm afraid I can't agree with you there. That's a lot more than we can afford.
6 A: We just have to invest more in our Belgian plant.
 B: That's out of the question, I'm afraid. It's far too inefficient. We should close it down.

11.7

1 Can I just ask a question at this point? You were telling us why the economy in Asia and South America remains difficult. Could you go over what you said about the Far East again, please, and tell us what the prospects might be in the next two years?
2 Sorry, could I stop you there for a moment? I'd like to go back to something you said earlier about your ability to deliver high profits regardless of market conditions. Could you be a little more specific about what you mean by 'high profits' and tell us exactly how much pre-tax profit you expect?
3 If I may interrupt, there's something I'm not sure I fully understood. You said you expected a 10% increase in sales next year. Could you elaborate on that and explain how you think such an increase can be achieved considering that the market in the region seems to have come to a halt?
4 If it's all right, there's a question I'd like to ask. When you were describing the plans for the restructuring of the Luxembourg plant, you hinted that redundancies were not unlikely. Could you tell us a bit more about the consequences of those plans and if possible specify how many people might be in danger of being laid off?
5 Sorry for cutting in on you. You said you were in favour of a limited licensing agreement. Could you specify what you mean by 'limited' please?

12 Strategy

12.1
hall; whole
court; coat

12.2
1 whole **6** broad
2 more **7** or
3 go **8** growing
4 those **9** important
5 approached **10** control

12.3
1 This product has been withdrawn from the market for eight months.
2 It might be re-launched at Easter.
3 You haven't contacted us for two weeks.
4 The meeting was due to start at nine.
5 Unibank is an obvious target for us for a merger.
6 We see no reason to change our position at this point.

12.4
1 to pe.ne.trate a mar.ket
2 to reach an ob.jec.tive
3 to de.ve.lop a stra.te.gy
4 to im.ple.ment a plan
5 to con.si.der a pro.po.sal
6 to dis.tri.bute a pro.duct
7 to ter.mi.nate a con.tract
8 to re.lo.cate a fac.tory
9 to ac.cept an of.fer
10 to a.ban.don a pro.ject

12.5
What we need is a new advertising strategy.

12.6
1 What they are particularly interested in is a joint venture.
2 What we intend to do is target the French market.
3 What he wants to do is restructure the Dortmund plant.
4 What we're not trying to do is change the whole procedure.
5 What they'd like to do is buy up a lot of shares quickly.

12.7
1 a) I'd like to hear your opinion on this.
 b) I would like to hear your opinion on this.
2 a) It hasn't been a success.
 b) It has not been a success.
3 a) We want to act.
 b) We do want to act.

12.8
1 It has made losses every year.
2 It will make a profit in the end.
3 Our products do not seem to appeal to French people.
4 That is a problem.
5 We do need a new strategy.

13 Culture

13.1
team

agree; deal; Japanese; reasons; strategic; three

13.2
1 They should have arrived at ten o'clock.
 /əv/
2 They shouldn't have sent such a young person to negotiate
 /əf/
 a contract in China.
3 He must have been disappointed by the food.
 /əv/

13.3
1 You might have tried to show more cultural sensitivity.
 /əf/
2 If they'd known their visitors were Muslims, they wouldn't have ordered pork for dinner.
 /əv/

3 If they'd planned their visit better, they wouldn't have

/əv/

begun the negotiation by announcing their deadlines.

13.4
1 A: Did you have a good time with your Lithuanian visitors?

B: Yes, I found them very friendly.

2 A: Did your Japanese visitors enjoy the reception?

B: Yes, ...but they thought it was rather noisy.

13.5
1 A: Looking forward to the meeting?

B: Yes.

2 A: Our new receptionist is doing well.

B: She's very efficient.

3 A: What was it like in Slovenia?

B: People were very sociable.

13.6
1 A: The seminar was very useful.

B: Was it?

C: Was it?

2 A: Their new Head is extremely efficient.

B: Is she?

C: Is she?

13.7
1 A: This is my first visit here.

B: Is it?

2 A: They've booked me into The Royal.

B: Have they?

3 A: There are lots of interesting concerts on at the moment.

B: Are there?

4 A: I'd be interested in a walk round the Old Town.

B: Would you?

5 A: I'm free tomorrow evening.

B: Are you?

13.8
1 We strongly recommend their new XJ3 ink-jet printer.
2 We deeply regret the inconvenience this error has caused you.
3 We will vigorously oppose plans for a joint venture.
4 I honestly believe we should give them more incentives.

14 Leadership

14.1
think; this
both; smooth

14.2
1	wealth	**6**	father
2	that	**7**	with
3	together	**8**	thing
4	breadth	**9**	three
5	their	**10**	thrive

14.3
1 I'd like you to prepare a report.
2 We think it's a wonderful deal.
3 Shouldn't we consult the others?
4 We'd all benefit from a joint venture.
5 As far as I'm concerned, we shouldn't accept a lower price.

14.4
1 Shall we bring forward our annual meeting to 30 November?

2 There is another seminar on Thursday, 23 of August.

3 They have postponed their visit until the 13th.

4 Why is 5 April such an important date?

5 Let's meet at 10.30 on Tuesday, 9 June.

14.5
1 a) decisive **b)** aggressive **c)** sensitive
2 a) passionate **b)** impulsive **c)** flexible
3 a) charismatic **b)** motivating **c)** sympathetic
4 a) accessible **b)** energetic **c)** adventurous
5 a) moderate **b)** thoughtful **c)** sincere

14.6
1 The manager who trusts his staff [pause] will make a good leader.
2 The manager, [pause] who trusts his staff, [pause] will make a good leader.

14.7
1 The local investors who opposed the deal [pause] are now feeling sorry.
2 The local investors, [pause] who opposed the deal, [pause] are now feeling sorry.
3 We should discontinue production of the lightweight models which are no longer in big demand.
4 We should discontinue production of the lightweight models, [pause] which are no longer in big demand.
5 He says his sister who lives in Paris [pause] is a born leader.
6 He says his sister, [pause] who lives in Paris, [pause] is a born leader.

14.8
1 A: What's a profit and loss account?
B: It's an account which shows a company's revenue and expenditure.
2 A: What's a head-hunter?
B: It's someone who tries to persuade someone to leave their job and accept a job with a different company.

3 A: What do you mean by intangible assets?
   B: They are assets which are difficult to quantify, like trade marks or patents, for instance.
4 A: What's an ombudsman?
   B: It's someone who works for the government or for an organisation, and deals with the complaints made against it.

15 Competition

15.1
1 **a)** share   b) unfair   c) fierce
2 **a)** leader   b) compete   c) heavy
3 **a)** tough   b) although   c) follow
4 **a)** average   b) advantage   c) unique
5 **a)** aggressive   b) firm   c) dirty
6 **a)** rival   b) adapt   c) challenge

15.2
breadth; dealer; heard; heavy; leader; real; threat

15.3
1 She is going to apply for a new job.
2 What time will these visitors be arriving?
3 I am meeting a new client tomorrow at ten o'clock.
4 There are clear signs that they are going to go bankrupt.
5 Are you staying to watch my presentation this afternoon?
6 The plane for Rome leaves at 9.30.
7 The company will be 20 years old next Wednesday.
8 They will be leaving the day after tomorrow.
9 The agreement will expire in 20 months' time.
10 The train arrives at 14.45.

15.4
1 The sources of cost advantage are <u>varied</u> and <u>depend</u> on the <u>structure</u> of the industry.
2 The means of differentiation are <u>peculiar</u> to <u>each</u> industry.
3 Differentiation can be based on the <u>product</u> itself, the de<u>li</u>very system by which it is sold, the <u>marketing</u> approach and a broad range of <u>other</u> factors.
4 Focus rests on the <u>choice</u> of a <u>narrow</u> competitive scope with<u>in</u> an industry.
5 A firm that engages in <u>each</u> strategy but fails to achieve <u>any</u> of them is stuck in the middle.

15.5
A: Good morning, Chris. David Olsen here. When can I see you about the trade fair.
B: Good morning, David. Let me just have a look at my diary. Erm … When would be a convenient time for you?
A: Well, Monday afternoon would be perfect.
B: I'm afraid I'm briefing our new sales reps then, but I'm free in the morning.
A: That's no good, I'm afraid. How about Tuesday morning?
B: I'm showing some Korean visitors around the factory then.
A: Well, Wednesday afternoon would suit me fine.
B: I'm afraid I'm giving a presentation at our sales conference but I'm free in the morning.
A: I can't make Wednesday morning. Thursday morning, maybe?
B: I'm visiting our Antwerp plant in the morning. But how about the afternoon? I could see you when I get back, say 2 pm?
A: Thursday at 2 pm. Great! I'll see you then.

15.6
1 A: We'll have to give them a discount.
   B: Yes, we certainly <u>will</u> have to give them more favourable terms.
2 A: We'll have to give them a discount.
   B: Actually I'm not sure we <u>will</u> have to give them more favourable terms.

15.7
1 A: Don't you think we should alter the specifications?
   B: Yes, we certainly <u>should</u> alter them.
2 A: It looks as if we'll need a different strategy.
   B: Yes, we certainly <u>will</u> need a different strategy.
3 A: It'll be quicker to fax them.
   B: Yes, it certainly <u>will</u> be quicker.
4 A: It seems they are expecting a reply by Thursday.
   B: Yes, they definitely <u>are</u> expecting a reply by then.

15.8
1 A: The lightweight model would be too expensive.
   B: Well, I'm not sure it <u>would</u> be too expensive, actually.
2 A: Their prices will go up from March 1st.
   B: Actually I'm not sure they <u>will</u> increase from March 1st.
3 A: The printer is now working properly.
   B: Well, I'm not sure it <u>is</u> working properly, actually.
4 A: The rate of exchange is going to increase again, it seems.
   B: Well, I'm not sure it <u>is</u> going to go up, actually.

16 Quality

16.1
ex.pec.<u>ta</u>.tion; ex.pla.<u>na</u>.tion; re.com.men.<u>da</u>.tion
dis.il.<u>lu</u>.sion; su.per.<u>vi</u>.sion; de.<u>ci</u>.sion

16.2
1 e.li.mi.<u>na</u>.tion
2 va.ri.<u>a</u>.tion
3 com.pen.<u>sa</u>.tion
4 pre.<u>ci</u>.sion

16.3
Rolls-<u>Royce</u> duly went <u>bust</u> in <u>nineteen</u> <u>seventy-three</u>. The <u>trouble</u> with <u>old</u>-style quality, it seemed, was
                                                    /wəz/
that <u>it</u> en<u>couraged</u> <u>supply</u>-driven <u>management</u>. The engineers would make the product to the <u>highest</u> possible <u>standard</u> and <u>price</u> it <u>accordingly</u>. If the public was so
                                                    /wəz/
un<u>cultured</u> that they turned <u>it</u> <u>down</u>, <u>so</u> much the <u>worse</u> for
                                                    /fə/
the public. And <u>so</u> old-style quality got <u>a</u> <u>bad</u> name <u>in</u> business circles. It was <u>all</u> very well for <u>artists</u> to produce
                /wəz/   /fər/
<u>masterpieces</u>. The job <u>of</u> <u>companies</u> was to <u>please</u> the
              /əv/   /wəz/
<u>market</u>.

16.4
1 A: I was promised delivery ten days ago and the goods still haven't arrived.

B: I'm very sorry there's been a delay. I'll look into the matter straightaway.

2 A: We've just received an invoice for goods we never ordered.

B: Oh dear! Sorry to hear that. Could you give me the reference number?

3 A: I'm afraid I'm still waiting for that fax your Sales Manager promised to send yesterday morning.

B: I'm afraid he isn't in at the moment, but I'll make sure he gets back to you as soon as possible.

4 A: The photocopier you delivered last week doesn't seem to work properly.

B: Sorry to hear that. What exactly seems to be the problem?

16.5

Would you like to start?

16.6

1 a) Could you explain what you mean by quality?

b) Could you explain what you mean by quality?

2 a) Would you mind going over that again?

b) Would you mind going over that again?

3 a) Excuse me. Could you repeat your example?

b) Excuse me. Could you repeat your example?

4 a) Could we get back to the main point?

b) Could we get back to the main point?

5 a) Could we move on to the next point?

b) Could we move on to the next point?

6 a) Excuse me. Could I come in here?

b) Excuse me. Could I come in here?

7 a) Sorry, I didn't quite follow you. Could you explain that again?

b) Sorry, I didn't quite follow you. Could you explain that again?

16.7
1 Could you explain what you mean by quality?
2 Would you mind going over that again?
3 Excuse me. Could you repeat your example?
4 Could we get back to the main point?
5 Could we move on to the next point?
6 Excuse me. Could I come in here?
7 Sorry, I didn't quite follow you. Could you explain that again?